PENGUIN BOOKS

ON THE SPOT

Albie Fiore studied architecture at Southend School of Architecture and the Architectural Association in London. After initially working in architecture, he worked as a chef on private yachts in the Mediterranean, ran an antique business specializing in old penny-arcade slot machines, of which he has a collection, and later became editor of *Games and Puzzles* magazine. He spent several years as production editor of *White Dwarf* magazine and as production manager and product designer for a games company. During this time, he also wrote *Shaping Rubik's Snake*, published by Penguin.

Together with Ian Bailey and Ian Waddelow, he has recently co-founded *Hatch*, a design and production group.

ON THE SPOT

DEVISED AND PRODUCED BY

WRITTEN AND EDITED BY

ALBIE FIORE

OTHER CONTRIBUTORS: BRUCE ALEXANDER,
IAN BAILEY, ANNE BEECH,
CHRISTIE CAMPBELL, MARGARET HICKEY,
SIMON NORFOLK, CAROLINE REED,
KATE SHAUGHNESSY, IAN WADDELOW

PENGUIN BOOKS

Penguin Books Ltd, Harmondsworth, Middlesex, England
Viking Penguin Inc., 40 West 23rd Street, New York, New York 10010, U.S.A.
Penguin Books Australia Ltd, Ringwood, Victoria, Australia
Penguin Books Canada Limited, 2801 John Street, Markham, Ontario, Canada L3R 1B4
Penguin Books (N.Z.) Ltd, 182–190 Wairau Road, Auckland 10, New Zealand

First published 1986

Typeset, printed and bound in Great Britain by
Hazell Watson & Viney Limited,
Member of the BPCC Group,
Aylesbury, Bucks
Typeset in 9/10pt Times Linotron 202

TO KATE
AND QUESTIONS WITHOUT ANSWERS

CONTENTS

AUTHOR'S NOTE

This book is intended primarily as a social diversion and entertainment. However, if in the process it causes some people to reappraise their own attitudes, then that will make the effort of preparing it that bit more worthwhile.

INTRODUCTION

Almost every day, you, and a million others, are faced with minor questions of choice. Normally, there is no problem. But sometimes, just sometimes, you may find yourself caught between the devil and the deep blue sea: torn between two equal choices. Damned if you do, and damned if you don't, but you must decide one way or the other.

It is these dilemmas that bring out the best, or the worst, in everyone.

This book presents you with just those situations. You can play it as a game, ask each other questions just for fun, or simply browse through the book on your own.

Some of the dilemmas are commonplace; others are bizarre. They will all, however, put you and your friends to the test. When it comes to the crunch, who will turn out to be unprincipled?

PART I

HOW TO PLAY

READING THE QUESTIONS

This book contains over 1,000 individual questions organized into over 200 'scenarios'. The scenarios either develop the initial plot or modify it in some way. When reading a question, read only the first part. Once this has been answered, the answer will determine the next question in the scenario as indicated on the particular page. This second question is a 'follow-up' question. The answer to this will either lead to another follow-up question or end that particular scenario. In effect, the sequence ends when the person answering the question changes their answer from one step to the next. For example, they answer 'yes' to the first question and then 'no' to the follow-up. The scenario also ends when someone answers the same right through the individual questions in that scenario, for example, they answer 'no' to all the questions.

To summarize, first read the initial question. You will be presented with a 'yes' or 'no' option. Decide what you would do in that situation. Once you have decided, read the next question in the sequence as indicated by the arrows on the page related to the answer that has been chosen.

FILLING IN THE DETAILS

Care has been taken to present the questions so that they can be asked by anyone of anyone. However, it is almost impossible to cover all the situations that can occur. Thus, in some of the questions, you must use your imagination to fill in the missing details. For example, a question may say 'someone of the opposite sex to you'. Obviously, when reading the question to yourself or someone else, you can substitute male or female as appropriate. Other situations may require a little more thought. Always try to tailor the question to the person answering it, so that the situation presented could apply to them.

If you are playing as a group, open discussion of these points as the questions are read will promote more discussion and add reality and spice to the dilemma.

There is only one rule on filling in any details on a question: it must be done so that the question applies specifically to the person who is to answer it.

You will find further notes on this aspect in the Special Notes section of the game rules.

ANSWERING THE QUESTIONS

The questions have been carefully worded to try not to presume any specific attitude on the part of the person answering the question. For example, you will not find any questions that say, 'You have been a lifelong supporter of the Conservative party when . . .'. Instead, the question might say, 'the party that you voted for at the last election'. Possibly the person answering the question will be the only one who knows which party that is. They must mentally supply such details as the question is read to them so that they can easily imagine themselves in the situation presented by the question.

Imagination is the key word. The answering player should never think, 'I'd never be in that situation.' They should imagine circumstances applicable to them whereby they could find themselves in that situation. They must try to make the dilemma as pertinent to themselves as they can. They can then decide more honestly what they would do in that situation.

Just as beauty is in the eye of the beholder, in this game everything is in the eye of the player answering the question. If someone is described as 'suspicious', the answering player must picture what they consider suspicious. Just as the person asking the question must fill in details as required, so must the answering player.

Each dilemma must seem as real as possible to the person answering it. Once this has been done, the answering player can then imagine more easily the situation as applied to them.

When all the details have been provided, the answering player should be limited to the 'yes' or 'no' answer as proposed by the question.

PLAYING THE GAME

PREPARATION AND EQUIPMENT

All that is needed to play On the Spot is a pack of ordinary playing cards, some paper, a pencil and a group of willing people, sober or otherwise.

Each player should be given one card of the heart suit and one of the spade suit. During the game hearts will represent 'yes' and spades 'no'. (If there are more than thirteen players, simply use red and black cards. If you don't happen to have a pack of cards handy, then use coins with heads for 'yes' and tails for 'no', or any other convenient method that the players choose.)

One player is elected scorer and should keep track of the score during the game.

RULES AND SEQUENCE OF PLAY

1. The player whose book this is has first turn.
2. The player on turn opens the book at random to a question page. If necessary, the player to their left then calls 'left' or 'right' to determine from which page the question will be asked.
3. The player on turn then selects which player will answer the question and reads the question to them.
4. The player who has been asked the question then answers it by placing a card face down in front of them. A heart equals 'yes', a spade equals 'no'. Before doing this, the answering player may call 'Depends' (see Additional Notes).
5. All players, except the answering player, may then discuss the question and how they think the answering player might have answered. The answering player can close this discussion by calling 'Time'. This can only be done after at least two people have spoken on the issues raised or nobody chooses to say anything more.
6. All players, other than the answering player, then place a card face down in front of them as to how they think the answering player has answered: a heart equals 'yes', a spade equals 'no'.
7. Once those players have all made their guess, the cards are revealed. Last of all, the answering player's card is revealed.

SCORING

8. All players who guessed correctly score one point.
9. The answering player scores one point *only if* the majority of players correctly guessed their answer or the guesses were evenly split between 'yes' and 'no'. If the majority of other players guess incorrectly, the answering player scores nothing.

THE FOLLOW-UP QUESTIONS

10. The player on turn then asks the same answering player the follow-up question

which is determined by the answer to the previous question. Play proceeds as for steps 4 to 9.

11.   If there are no more follow-up questions *OR* the answering player gives an answer which is marked 'question ends', the player on turn passes the book to the next player on the left, who is now on turn. The new player on turn proceeds as before from step 1, selecting a new question and answering player.

WINNING

12.   The game is played for an agreed length of time. At the end of that time, the player with the most points is the winner.

NOTE

If the same question is selected more than once in a game, it should still be asked. However, it cannot be asked of somebody who has already answered the particular question in that game.

Also, some questions indicate by a note at the top that they must be asked of a specific person, for example, 'smoker'. If nobody of that category is playing the game, select a new question.

ADDITIONAL NOTES

Care has been taken to present the questions to elicit only a 'yes' or 'no' answer. It is impossible, though, to cover all eventualities for all people. Part of the fun of the game will come in dressing the questions to suit the players. This happens when the answering player calls 'Depends'.

Depends

The answering player must eventually answer 'yes' or 'no' to the question. Before they do this, they may call 'Depends' and ask for further specific information. For example, they may ask, 'Is this "friend" male or female?'

This process in itself will be quite revealing. Normally, the sex of the 'friend' would not matter. But to this player it does! It is up to the player asking the question to embellish it appropriately. First, the follow-up questions should be glanced at to ensure that there will be no duplication. For example, if one of the follow-ups introduces the fact that the 'friend' is someone of the opposite sex and to whom the answering player has always been attracted, then the 'friend' in the initial question cannot be of that type.

The player asking the question is thus free to embellish it in any way they see fit to suit the answering player; however, they must avoid duplicating or contradicting anything that is to arise in a follow-up question.

The additional information must be tailored to eliminate all possibilities other than the 'yes' and 'no' answers.

Calling time

The answering player, although not permitted to take part in the discussion of the issues raised, in fact chairs the discussion. After a reasonable time, the answering player can call 'Time' and end the discussion. They can do this if they feel that it is becoming too repetitious or even embarrassing. (In reality, the answering player can join in the discussion, so long as they do not give away what their answer is. Also, the answering player should not join in any discussion about why they answered a certain way until *after* the sequence of questions has ended. This is to prevent them from inadvertently pre-empting an answer to one of the following questions.)

EXAMPLE OF PLAY

Andy, Beatrice, Carol, David, Erica and Fred are playing. Carol is the one with the *savoir-faire* to have bought the book and so has first turn. She opens the book at random. David, on her left, calls 'right', so Carol looks at the question on the right-hand page. It reads as follows:

QUESTION

You are away from home and staying in a hotel. One evening, as you return to the hotel, you find a £10 note caught up in some rumpled carpet behind the entrance doors. The receptionist happens to be looking your way, though not at you. Nobody else is around and you're not short of money. Do you hand the £10 note in?

 YES   **NO**

Before you can pick up the money, the phone rings and the receptionist turns away to answer it. Do you now hand in the money?

 YES | NO *Question ends* |

On another occasion, you are leaving the hotel when you find a £10 note in the hotel car park. There is nobody else around. Do you go back and hand it in?

As you pass, the receptionist asks if you found anything as they thought they saw you pick something up. They explain that another guest dropped their handbag a short while ago and the contents had scattered everywhere. After a quick and not very thorough search, they had had to dash off as they were in a hurry, so there could still be some of their things lying around. You could easily and plausibly say that you were straightening the rumpled carpet. However, do you now hand in the £10 note?

 NO | YES *Question ends* |

On another occasion, you are just coming into the hotel when you see the guest entering just in front of you drop a £10 note. They are not aware of the fact. They are a few yards in front of you with their back to you. Nobody else is around and the receptionist is looking the other way. Do you tell the person that they have dropped the money?

Carol quickly reads through the question, and decides to ask Fred. She reads Fred the initial question. Fred's immediate response is, 'Depends'.

'Depends on what?' ask Erica and Andy almost simultaneously.

'Well, is the receptionist an attractive woman?'

Carol, realizing that the question is about honesty rather than anything else, decides that the receptionist is male and not attractive to Fred.

Fred seems disappointed at this news, but continues, 'How's the service been at this place?'

Once again, Carol decides that this should not have any bearing on the basic issue. She replies, 'Professional and adequate. You've got nothing to complain about, but, on the other hand, it's nothing to write home about either. OK. Do you hand in the money? You can hear a car pulling up outside the hotel, so you'd better decide quickly!'

Fred promptly places one of his two cards face down on the table. The discussion is brief and not very animated. The general consensus is that most people would pocket the money. Erica, however, would be inclined to hand it in. The discussion turns to how Fred might react and David laughs and begins to tell of a time when he and Fred were students in Brighton. Fred quickly calls 'Time' before David can elaborate.

All the players then place one of their cards face down to indicate how they think Fred has answered. When they have done this, Fred reveals his card. A spade – no, he would not hand in the money. Everybody else reveals their cards. All of them have guessed correctly. Everybody, including Fred, should score a point but David who's feeling lazy doesn't bother to enter that score. Beatrice laughingly chides Fred and says, 'You gave it away. You spent so much time looking for reasons why you might hand it in, that it was obvious what you would do.' Fred blames it on the receptionist.

Carol then reads Fred the question that follows on from his 'no' answer. Fred ponders to himself whether the guest who dropped the money might be an old lady but decides that if he were to ask the receptionist, he could hardly claim not to have found anything. He is also sure of what he would do and so places a card face down on the table, rather than say 'depends' and risk revealing his course of action again.

The others then discuss the new situation. This time they are evenly split on what they might do. However, the point is what they think Fred would do. They don't get far on this before David mentions Brighton and Fred calls 'Time'.

The others place their cards on the table and then reveal them. David and Erica guess that Fred would now hand in the money. The others all think otherwise. Fred reveals his card: a heart – yes, he would now hand in the money. Fred curses, since as the majority thought otherwise, he scores nothing. However, David and Erica each score a point for knowing Fred well enough to guess his answer correctly. David chuckles, 'I knew he'd take the money, but I knew that he wouldn't lie if anybody asked him about it.'

Since Fred has changed his answer from 'no' to 'yes', the 'yes' is marked 'Question ends', so there is no follow-up question and Carol passes the book to David. It is now David's turn to ask someone a question. He opens the book . . .

PART 2

THE QUESTIONS

QUESTION 1

You are at the house of two close friends helping them clear some junk from their loft. You come across an old, framed painting. The painting is amateurish and awful. The frame is marvellous and you like it very much. You have a picture at home that needs framing and this would be perfect. You mention it to your friends. One tells you that it belonged to a distant relative of theirs and that although they don't like it, they'd rather hang on to it. However, once that friend has left the room, the other one says, 'Take no notice of them. If you like it, take it. We're supposed to be clearing this junk out. If they had their way, we'd never get rid of anything. I'll put this down by the door later. Just pick it up as you leave. They'll never even notice that it's gone.' Both of the two are equally your friend, you have no leaning towards one or the other. As you leave, the painting is beside the door. Your friends are still up in the loft. Do you take the painting?

 YES

A day or so later, you take it and the picture that you want placed in the frame to a picture-framer. Later, he calls you. He has removed the old painting to find, from the part concealed by the frame, that it is painted over the top of another older painting that looks to be the work of a minor artist. He thinks that the work would be worth about £1,000 to £2,000. Rather than tell the friend who gave you the painting, do you just keep quiet about it?

YES | NO *Question ends* |

A little later, your friend phones you. The other friend has noticed that the frame has gone. They've had a slight argument and the upshot is that the one who wanted to keep the frame in the first place wants it back. They're not angry with you, just with their partner for giving it away against their wishes. Since they are only interested in the frame, you can easily give it back and keep the painting claiming that it had been thrown away during the framing of your picture. Do you do this, or something similar, so as to return the frame but not the painting?

 NO

You haven't gone far when you hear footsteps behind you. It is your friend who wanted to give you the painting. They have it under their arm. They tell you that you forgot it and ask you to take it. They add that if you don't, they'll only throw it in the dustbin at the next opportunity as some of the junk must be cleared out one way or the other. Do you now take the painting?

NO | YES *Question ends* |

In this instance, the painting belonged to a relative of the one who wants to give it to you and they are your friend. You hardly know their partner. Do you now take the painting?

28

QUESTION 2

You are single. You are at a party one evening. There is only one person there, of the opposite sex, whom you find attractive. Later, while talking to them, it becomes clear that they also find you equally attractive. However, they state quite clearly that they are happily married, but their partner happens to be away for the weekend. They also make it abundantly clear that they would like very much to spend this night with you as they find you so attractive. This is not something that they have ever done before, nor do they expect any lasting relationship. They seem quite happy with the idea of a one-night stand. You do not know them or their partner, though you do have some mutual friends. Do you accept their tacit offer?

 YES

The same situation except that their partner happens to be a workmate of yours. They are not a friend of yours but you see them every working day and occasionally have casual conversations with them. Do you still accept the offer?

 YES | **NO**   *Question ends* |

The same situation except that their partner is not a workmate but a very close friend of yours of long standing. However, for one reason or another, this is the first time that you have met their spouse who, from the conversation, has not placed you as a friend of their partner. Do you still accept the offer?

 NO

The same situation except that the two of you have no mutual friends whatsoever. Do you now accept the offer?

NO | **YES**   *Question ends* |

The same situation, except that the person is not married. However, they are, and have been for some years, living with a partner in what they describe as an 'open' relationship. Do you accept the offer?

QUESTION 3   (male)

Your country is involved in a war in the Far East, much the same, and for the same reasons, as the Vietnam War. There is conscription. However, you are exempted as you are a student on a university or college course. You are about to sit the exams at the end of your first year. If you pass you will be able to continue your course. However, if you fail you will not be able to resit any exams as you will receive your call-up papers for service in the war in the same post as your exam results. This has already happened to everybody you know who has failed an exam. You are an average student. It is fifty-fifty whether you will pass or fail. Do you attempt to cheat in the exam?

YES

NO

Despite cheating, you have no idea how well you have done. You know that you have done neither really well nor really badly. You think that you have done just enough to pass, but you can't be sure. You hear, through the grapevine, who the examiner is and that 'for a consideration' they are willing to upgrade any borderline candidates to ensure that they pass. However, the sums mentioned would involve all the money you have plus selling or pawning practically everything you own. Do you do this to bribe the examiner?

You sit the exam. You have no idea how you've done. You could pass, equally you could fail. Conscientious objectors are being given up to five years in jail. However, if you enlist voluntarily before your exam results, you can join the navy which is not involved in the war. This would mean doing service in the Mediterranean for three years no matter what your exam result is. Do you enlist in the navy?

NO | **YES**   *Question ends* |

YES | **NO**   *Question ends* |

The same situation, except that there is no way that you could raise the money except to steal it. Would you steal the money to bribe the examiner?

You learn that some friends are planning to skip the country and dodge the call-up. However, they must skip before the exam results as otherwise there is no way of leaving the country. This means spending an indeterminate time abroad. You have the chance to do the same. Do you skip the country?

QUESTION 4

You are walking through a local park that is particularly well kept and beautiful, when you see a young teenager screwing up some fish and chip papers and throwing them on the grass. There is a litter bin only a few yards away. The boy is not particularly large or rough-looking. Do you suggest he should pick them up and put them in the bin?

 YES   **NO**

He refuses and tells you to pick it up yourself if you're so worried. He stands and watches you. Do you pick up the litter in front of him?

The teenager then goes up to the bin and starts rummaging in it, throwing all the contents out on to the grass. Do you tell him to stop and pick up the litter?

 YES | NO   *Question ends* | **NO** | YES   *Question ends* |

He takes it out of the bin and throws it back on the grass. Laughing, he tells you to pick it up again. Knowing he will probably throw it out again, and knowing that he will refuse to pick it up himself, do you pick it up and take it off to another bin?

He pulls a bottle out of the bin and, leaving the litter all over the grass, starts kicking the bottle around. He is kicking it towards a hard area nearby where children play and on which the bottle could easily shatter. Do you now tell him to stop and, at least, put the bottle back in the bin?

QUESTION 5

You are just approaching your front door late at night. You hear footsteps approaching fast. You turn to see a young, respectable man running towards you. As he nears you he says, 'Excuse me, could I possibly use your phone to ring for an ambulance? There's an old tramp collapsed on the pavement over there. He's probably drunk, but he might need attention.' Across the road you can see someone lying on the pavement but it is too dark to see them clearly. As far as you can tell, the young man seems genuine. You are on your doorstep and you have a telephone. However, you know of a public call box just round the corner. Do you allow the young man into your home to make the phone call or while you make it yourself?

 YES   **NO**

The same situation except that the tramp that the young man claims to have found is just round the corner and consequently you can see no one lying on the pavement. Do you still allow the young man into your home to make the phone call or while you make the call yourself?

The same situation except that it is a summer's evening and there is enough light for you clearly to see a tramp lying on the pavement over the road. Do you now allow the young man into your home to make the phone call or while you make the call yourself?

 YES | NO   *Question ends* | **NO** | YES   *Question ends* |

As originally, you can see someone lying on the pavement in the gloom across the road, but this time there is no young man. Another tramp, slightly the worse for drink, is doing the asking. He is, however, polite and courteous and seems genuinely concerned about his collapsed friend. As far as you can tell, he seems genuine. Do you allow him into your home to make the phone call, or while you make it yourself?

Once again, it is too dark for you to see anything other than that there is someone lying on the pavement over the road. However, it is a respectable-looking young girl who has approached you. Do you allow her into your home to make the call or while you make the call yourself?

QUESTION 6

You have been having a quiet drink at home when the phone rings. It is a good friend who asks if you can drive out and help another friend with them who has broken a leg rather badly. The police are not involved and because of unusual circumstances, your friend tells you that they were told that an ambulance would be unable to reach them for about an hour. You are the only person they have been able to contact. You are about twenty minutes' drive away. However, you are pretty sure that you must be on the borderline of the breathalyser limit. It is a warm summer's evening just before lighting-up time. Do you drive out to help?

 YES   **NO**

When you get out into the fresh air, you realize that you are more drunk than you thought. You cannot now contact your friend who was phoning from a call box. Do you still drive out to help?

 YES | **NO**   *Question ends* |

You now know that you must be over the breathalyser limit. As you approach the scene of your friend's accident, a police car overtakes you. You hear the siren cut out shortly. Then, some distance away, you can see that the police are at the scene of the accident. Someone has obviously notified them. Do you still drive on to help?

As it happens, you know that the local police are heavily involved in a nearby pop concert. You are extremely unlikely to meet any on the way or near the scene of the accident. Do you now drive out to help?

NO | **YES**   *Question ends* |

In this instance, the friend who phoned you happens to be an off-duty policeman. He assures you, that under the circumstances he can almost guarantee that no action will be taken against you if any of the local police happen to catch you. Do you now drive out to help?

QUESTION 7

You inherit a plot of land in the country from a distant relative. It is a small area of wasteland that has planning permission for a small house to be built on it. You have the finance to do this and can make a considerable amount of money from doing so. Just prior to the site being cleared so that work on the building can begin, you visit the plot of land. While there, you happen to notice a strange butterfly. It is so spectacular that it excites your curiosity but you can find no reference to it in any books. It is obviously not a very common one. It could even be extremely rare or verging on extinction. You have no idea. Do you, however, proceed as planned and have the site cleared for building even though it will destroy the butterfly's habitat?

 YES

 NO

In this instance, the rare creature was not a butterfly, but a small shrew-like mammal. Once again, it lives on your land and could even be a protected species. Rather than find out, do you have the site cleared to commence work?

In this instance, it was not a butterfly, but a small, brightly coloured beetle. Once again, you could not identify it and it might even be a protected species for all you know. Do you proceed as planned and have the site cleared, regardless of the beetle's presence?

 YES | **NO** *Question ends*

This time it was a very rare bird that you could not identify. There is a nest on the site with eggs in it and indications that the bird nests there annually and has been doing so for some time. Once again, it could be a protected species. Do you still go ahead and have the site cleared immediately as planned?

 NO | **YES** *Question ends*

In this instance, it was not a butterfly or beetle, but a small, rather raggy weed. There was a clump of them. Their flowers were not very pretty but it was so unlike anything that you had seen before that it caught your attention. Once again, no research by you could identify it. Do you now go ahead and have the site cleared as planned, regardless of the rare weed?

QUESTION 8

Your work takes you abroad where you must live for a while. You are in a country where there is an internal armed struggle between the authorities and guerrillas (terrorists/freedom fighters, as you will). The guerrillas have the support of a large portion of the population and you happen to be in sympathy with their cause and objectives. You are working in a remote part of the country where you have been welcomed by the locals and have made many friends. One day, you discover that many of the locals and your friends are actually involved in the terrorist movement. Later, you are due to travel to another part of the country. They ask you to deliver a verbal message to somebody there. They tell you that it is important and involved with their struggle. Do you agree to do this?

YES

You deliver the message and your friends welcome your involvement with their cause. You are next asked to help more actively. As a foreigner you are unlikely to be stopped by security forces so they ask you on your next journey to take some spare weapon parts with you. You are to deliver them to another village on your route. Do you agree to do this?

YES | **NO** *Question ends*

The town where you are is growing as a centre for the terrorists. You are next introduced to their bomb factory. They need some booby-trap bombs quickly. You are asked to help in their manufacture. They will only be used against military personnel. Do you agree to do this?

YES | **NO** *Question ends*

The terrorists are winning. As they prepare for their final push, you are asked to bear arms, an automatic rifle, in a raid. Do you agree to take part in the armed raid and carry a weapon?

NO

Your friends tell you that the message is simply a warning that the security forces are planning a raid on a certain village. Many women and children may be killed. You are again asked to deliver the message. Do you agree?

NO | **YES** *Question ends*

You must still make the trip for reasons of work. On your way there, the security forces stop you. As you are a foreigner, they are polite and formal. You are taken to their headquarters and asked a few questions. You are asked if you know of any terrorists in the town where you are working. Do you lie and say that you do not?

QUESTION 9

You find yourself stranded five miles from your destination on a fairly busy road out in the country. There are no taxis or buses. Dusk will be falling soon and the weather is dull and cloudy. It looks as though it might rain soon. The only choice you have is to walk or hitch a lift. Do you try to hitch a lift?

YES

NO

The same situation, except that there have been several stories in the press recently concerning a series of murders in this area known as the 'Hitch-Hike Killings'. The victims have been of both sexes but all were hitch-hikers. Do you still try to hitch a lift?

 YES | NO   *Question ends*

The most recent of the 'Hitch-Hike Killings' was over a week ago. An ordinary family saloon pulls up as you hitch. The driver is a fairly average middle-aged man. However, he does not say where he is heading but asks you where you are going. He then says that that is where he happens to be heading. During this, he seems disinclined to look you in the eye. Do you accept his offer of a lift?

As you walk, a car pulls up. In it are a young couple who seem friendly enough. They ask if you'd like a lift. Do you accept their offer of a lift?

 NO | YES   *Question ends*

The same situation, except that in the back of the young couple's car are two children aged about four and six. Do you now accept their offer of a lift?

QUESTION 10   (male)

You happen to pop into a pub in an area far from where you live. An acquaintance of yours turns out to be in there so you chat and enjoy a drink together. There is a rowdy gang of about eight toughs in the bar who seem to be looking for trouble. You are standing at the bar when they happen to pass by. For some reason, possibly because you're not a local face, they start to pick on you. Despite anything you say, they throng around you and pin you to the bar. One throws a punch at you that hits you firmly in the mouth and breaks a tooth. Your mouth starts to bleed a bit. Just then, your acquaintance, whom you do not know very well, grabs the person who hit you and tells them to lay off. The group turns on him, saying, 'Oh, you want some trouble then, do you, mate?' For the moment, they have forgotten you. There is an exit nearby through which you could now slip out. Do you do so?

 YES

 NO

As you do so, two big men by the door get up and face you. However, they are offering their help. They start towards the group obviously expecting you to wade in alongside them. You are slightly behind them. They cannot see you. Do you still try to slip out?

One of the group punches your acquaintance but misses as the blow is dodged. Incensed by this, the assailant grabs a bottle and tries to smash it against the bar. Four of the group turn towards you. They look for bottles to use as weapons against you. Do you now run out of the door behind you?

 YES

| **NO**   *Question ends* |

One of the two who have decided to help you turns and says . . . well, in no uncertain terms they tell you that you're chicken and various other unmentionables for leaving your friend to 'those nutters'. They then attempt to grab you to drag you into the fight that is now starting. Do you still dash out of the door?

 NO

| **YES**   *Question ends* |

Just then there is a shout; your acquaintance has vaulted the pool table and managed to escape through another exit. The entire group rushes after him, forgetting you. They have all left the pub and you hear them running off down the street outside. They fade into the distance. Do you now slip out and go home rather than waiting to find out whether your acquaintance is all right?

QUESTION 11

You are at your partner's flat. They have just popped out to pick up some shopping. While idling around, you notice their diary. Do you glance through it?

YES

You notice that another person's name crops up regularly. A person the same sex as you. You have never heard of this person and your partner has never mentioned them. You notice that in a few days' time there is another entry with the same name, a time and the name of a pub. Do you deliberately suggest that you and your partner go out that evening to see what their reaction is?

YES | NO   *Question ends* |

Your partner tells you that that evening is out of the question as they have something arranged. They do not tell you what. The pub in question is known to you and is not too far from your flat. Do you happen to pop in there 'by chance' on the evening in question?

NO

Later that evening, your partner tells you that they must break an arrangement that you had next week as something has cropped up. They seem evasive as to what and give no more information than that.

They pop out again. The diary is still there. Do you now glance through it?

NO | YES   *Question ends* |

Your partner has been more unavailable than ever lately. Several times they have either broken arrangements that they had with you or have been busy on dates that you suggest.

Once again, you are at their flat while they have popped out. Do you now glance through their diary?

QUESTION 12

You are tidying up when you come across one of your all-time favourite books. It is a hardback novel. As you browse through it, you realize it is, in fact, a library book which is now nine months overdue. You have never had a reminder so the library may well have forgotten about it. Your library has a maximum fine policy, so you know that the most you will have to pay is £2. You are not short of cash. Do you return the library book?

YES

NO

As you prepare to take it back, you catch sight of the cover price: £4. You know that if you lose a library book, you must pay half the cover price which in this case is the same as the fine you could have to pay for returning it. It is your favourite book and is not available in print at the moment. Do you still return the book?

YES

| NO   Question ends |

In this instance, the book is not a novel but a very expensive, large-format art book full of full-colour plates of the works of your favourite artist. The book would be very hard to come by normally. Do you return this book to the library?

A letter arrives from the library. It says that, due to an error during computerization, they are having a great deal of difficulty in tracking down overdue books. It appeals for people to be honest and return any overdue books as soon as possible. Do you return the book?

NO

| YES   Question ends |

A second letter arrives saying that according to their old records, you have an overdue book. It asks for its return. Do you return the book?

QUESTION 13

You are due to fly out for your annual month's holiday. Everything is arranged and paid for in advance. Three hours before take-off, your elderly widowed mother rings up to say that she is feeling very ill and wants you to go to her immediately. You have always been on good terms with her, though she has become a bit of a hypochondriac in her old age. However, she has never done anything like this before. You know that the flights are heavily booked and that if you miss this one, you may well end up having to cancel your holiday. You have no brothers or sisters. Do you, however politely, refuse to go to your mother rather than miss your plane?

 YES

 NO

YES — You fly out as planned but when you arrive at your hotel there is a telegram awaiting you. Your mother has been taken into hospital. When you telephone the hospital, you are told that your mother is in for observation. Nobody, as yet, knows how serious her condition is. Do you continue your holiday, regardless of whether you stay in touch with the hospital or not, rather than fly home immediately?

NO — You rush to her bedside to discover that she only has a mild touch of flu. She confesses to having been depressed at the thought of you being away for a month, adding that she feels particularly lonely and vulnerable at the moment. She asks you, if you could, not to go away on holiday this year but to spend it at home. Do you refuse to do this?

 NO

YES *Question ends*

The following year, you have booked to fly off on holiday for a well-deserved break. However, on the day of your departure, just a couple of hours before your flight, a neighbour of your mother's phones to say that your mother is not well and is asking for you. Do you refuse to go to her this time?

 YES | **NO** *Question ends*

You learn from the hospital that your mother requires a small operation immediately. The operation is routine although because of your mother's age there is a small possibility of complications. The doctor politely suggests that it might be beneficial if you were at her bedside after the operation. This would mean abandoning your holiday after only a few days. Do you still decline to go to your mother's bedside?

QUESTION 14

While you are sitting in your local pub, someone approaches you and offers you a very expensive watch at a dirt-cheap price. The person claims to be selling it for a friend who has been made redundant and is short of cash. It is a particular watch that you have always liked and wanted. However, you could never have afforded the proper price. You can, however, easily afford this one at the price at which it is being offered. Do you buy the watch from the stranger in the pub?

YES   **NO**

YES	NO
In the local newspaper a few days later you read that the police are looking for items stolen in a raid on a jeweller's shop. There were several watches of the type and brand that you bought in the pub. The police are asking the public to report anyone trying to sell items of this nature. Nobody was injured in the raid. Do you sit tight and keep quiet?	A few days later it is your birthday. Your partner gives you a present. It turns out to be the watch that you were offered in the pub the other night. Your partner is excited as they say that they know it is something that you have always wanted and they managed to pick one up really cheaply. Do you accept the gift?

YES | NO   *Question ends* | **NO** | YES   *Question ends* |

The same situation, except a shop assistant was badly and brutally beaten in the raid. Would you still sit tight and keep quiet?	Your partner decides to keep the watch themselves. A few days later, you are in your local pub. A policeman comes in and talks to the barman, who points to you. The policeman comes up and says that he believes that you were offered a watch a few evenings ago. He adds that it most likely came from a raid on a jeweller's store, in which nobody was injured. He asks you if you have any information. Do you tell him about the watch that your partner bought?

QUESTION 15

The previous occupant at your address left you with a forwarding address for their mail. A year has passed and you have not heard from them at all. A letter arrives for the previous occupant. It is typewritten but does not bear any official markings. It is totally anonymous. Do you forward it?

 YES

 NO

In this instance, the transaction when you took over from the previous occupant had been very acrimonious. Do you still forward the letter?

In this instance, the envelope is of personal-style stationery and the address is handwritten. Do you now forward the letter?

 YES | **NO** *Question ends*

NO | **YES** *Question ends*

In this instance, the transaction was acrimonious in that you were 'done' by the previous owner. This had cost you an extra £200 that you could ill afford. The letter in front of you looks as though it could well have a cheque in it. Now do you forward it?

In this instance, the previous occupant has been in touch with you. Six months ago, they sent you a change-of-address card with a note asking you to forward any mail to their new address. The note mentioned that there could be a letter from some friends abroad as the previous occupant had lost their address and not been able to inform them of their moves. The letter in front of you is handwritten and bears a foreign stamp. Do you now forward the letter?

 YES | **NO** *Question ends*

In this instance, there was no acrimony, but the letter in front of you looks to be some unsolicited junk mail. Do you forward this?

QUESTION 16 (male)

You are walking along a central city street when an attractive girl solicits you. For reasons of your own, you decline. However, a little further up the street, a man approaches you and identifies himself as a plain-clothes policeman. He asks if the girl solicited you and, if she did, whether you would swear to this in court. Do you tell the policeman the truth and agree to appear as a witness in court?

YES

The policeman then calls the girl over and tells her that she must accompany him to the police station. The girl begins to abuse the policeman in no uncertain terms and tells you that 'This bastard is out to get me because I won't give him free sex like the other girls do!' Do you still agree to act as witness so that the policeman can press charges?

YES | NO *Question ends* |

On the way to the police station, the girl manages to whisper to you, 'You know what this sod will do, he'll take your name and address before we get to the station, and tell you he'll contact you when you're needed. Then he'll want some money or sex off me. If I don't agree, then he'll contact you and press charges. If I do, you'll never hear from him.' Before you get anywhere near the police station, the policeman does this, insisting that it is entirely unnecessary for you to come any further. Do you still agree to act as a witness against the girl?

NO

The policeman explains that the girl is not a straightforward prostitute. She solicits people, takes a portion of money in advance and then agrees to meet them at a fictitious address. She is really a con-artist. He would like to get her off the street because of this. Do you now agree to appear as a witness?

NO | YES *Question ends* |

The same situation, except that the policeman's explanation is different. He tells you that she takes money in advance and agrees to meet her client at an address. When the client gets there, he is mugged by the girl's associates. The victims are disinclined to go to the police as the girl is skilled and only picks married men. The policeman would like to get her off the streets. Do you now agree to appear as a witness?

QUESTION 17

You are walking home late on a warm, dry, summer's night. It is very dark. As you pass some bushes by the pathside, you notice someone lying on the ground. It looks like a tramp. Do you stop to check if they are OK?

YES   **NO**

It is a tramp. There is an empty bottle nearby which has no label on it. The tramp is totally dead to the world. You can shout, prod him or shake him about all you want. You get no response. Do you now go and phone for an ambulance?

As you pass, you can see just enough to tell that it is a tramp. Just then, he groans and rolls over a bit. You can vaguely make out a dark mark on the side of his head. It could be a bruise, blood or just dirt. You can't tell without a closer look. Do you now stop to check if he is OK?

YES | NO   *Question ends* | **NO** | YES   *Question ends* |

The ambulance comes. The two ambulancemen are very friendly. When they see the tramp, they remark, 'It's old Jack again.' They shine a torch in his eyes and gently slap his face. After much patient prompting from them, he eventually wakes up a bit. They then say, 'Come on, you old sod, we'll get you a bed for the night in the hospital.' They help him into the ambulance. They thank you and tell you not to worry and then drive off.

A week later, in a similar situation, you come across old Jack again, unconscious by a tree with an empty bottle nearby. After similar initial responses to last time, do you again phone for an ambulance?

He rolls over. The mark on the side of his head starts to change shape and run downwards. It is liquid and most probably blood. From the position, it could easily have been done if he fell over in a drunken stupor. Do you, however, now stop to check whether he is OK?

QUESTION 18

A good friend in the country has recently moved house. They sent you a note of their change of address recently, but it seems to have been mislaid and you wish to write to them. You have searched everywhere, and the only remaining place that you can conceive that it might be is in the dustbin. There are no mutual friends from whom you could get their new address. The dustbins are communal. When you peek in, you see the most appallingly messy rubbish – tea leaves, rotten fruit, oily substances, fish skins, all mixed together. It is hot and there are plenty of flies around. Do you search through the dustbin for the address?

 YES

 NO

This time the missing piece of paper bears a phone number. You had recently been at a party where you met somebody to whom you were very much attracted. They had given you their number and asked you to call them. You had not had a chance to give them yours. Neither of you knew anyone at the party in common. Do you search through the rubbish for their phone number?

This time the missing document is a very important letter about your credit-worthiness that you have spent days eliciting from your bank manager. You need the letter badly to send to some other organization that has been waiting for it urgently to clinch a deal. You know that it will take days to get another copy from the bank. Do you now rummage through the rubbish in the dustbin?

 YES | **NO**   *Question ends* |

·**NO** | **YES**   *Question ends* |

This time, it's Christmas. You recently met someone on a friendly basis. You quite liked them. They have sent you a Christmas card. The piece of paper, probably lurking in the dustbin, bears their address. There is nobody you know in common and you can't even remember their surname to look in the telephone directory. Do you still search through the dustbin for their address?

In the post that morning you received a letter from the organization awaiting your letter. It said that unless they received your letter by return, the deal would be off. The deal is critical to you and you were relying on it. Do you now search through the dustbin?

QUESTION 19

You share a flat with your sister. Her sullen, unhelpful boyfriend begins to stay more and more frequently. He has partaken of many of your meals and knocked back plenty of your wine but never contributes any money or muscle. He has stored in your sister's room a large bottle of spirits, your favourite as it happens, for his own late-night consumption. One evening, a friend calls round after closing time for a chat. However, you have nothing alcoholic to offer them and you could both do with a drink. Your sister and her boyfriend are out but will be back some time in the wee hours. There is a late-night shop about twenty minutes away. Do you help yourself to a couple of drinks from the boyfriend's bottle?

 YES

 NO

As you go to do so, you notice that there is a pen mark on the label marking the current level in the bottle. Do you still help yourself to a couple of drinks?

 YES | **NO**   *Question ends* |

Afterwards, do you top up the bottle with water to bring the level back to the pen mark?

You pop out but the local late-night shop is closed. That was the only possible chance. On returning to your flat, you and your friend have a long chat. You both feel even more like a drink. Do you now go and help yourself to some of the boyfriend's drink?

 NO | **YES** *Question ends* |

While chatting with your friend, you suddenly realize that you do have some drink. After a party, while clearing up, you popped a part bottle of your favourite in the larder and have since forgotten about it. When you go to the larder, the bottle is there but with only a drop in the bottom. Someone has drunk it. It was not you and your sister never touches this particular drink. Do you now help yourself to some drinks from the boyfriend's bottle?

QUESTION 20

You are on holiday in a remote part of the world . . . very, very remote. You are captured by a group of particularly nasty local terrorists. You have never heard of them or their cause. There are other prisoners at their camp. The terrorists give you a large knife and order you to kill one of the other prisoners who is bound and unconscious. You are alone in a hut with the prisoner you must kill. There are five armed terrorists in the large and only doorway. There is no escape and no cover. The terrorists explain that the prisoner is one of their own who has betrayed them. By their own codes, they cannot shed the blood of one of their own. They are therefore ordering you to do it. Some of the other prisoners are of your nationality. They tell you that they have been well looked after and none of them has been harmed in any way. However, the terrorists now tell you that if you refuse to execute this prisoner, or in any way try to attack or deceive the terrorists, you will immediately be shot dead on the spot. From the prisoner's dress and appearance you can see that he is one of the terrorist group as they say. Do you kill him as you have been ordered?

 YES

 NO

In this instance, the prisoner is a woman of their group. Her 'crime' is that she committed adultery with someone from another tribe. She is in her mid-twenties. Do you kill her as the terrorists have ordered?

 YES | **NO** *Question ends* |

In this instance, the prisoner is a young child. She is about ten years old and is one of the terrorist group. Her crime was that she stole some food. Do you kill her as the terrorists have ordered?

The same situation except that the prisoner has committed murder. He killed another of the terrorist group in a drunken brawl. You saw this happen and know this man did commit that crime. Do you now kill him as the terrorists have ordered?

 NO | **YES** *Question ends* |

In this instance, the prisoner's crime is that he raped and brutally murdered a young girl of the group. Again, he is one of their own and you actually saw this horrific crime and know that the man is guilty. Do you now kill him as the terrorists have ordered?

QUESTION 21

You have just had a good meal with some close friends. In the course of an ensuing alcohol-fuelled discussion, your partner embroiders the truth somewhat. Only you know that what they have just said is untrue. What was said related to a close friend of yours who, as far as you know, is only vaguely known by the friends with whom you are talking. The statement was neither derogatory nor complimentary. It was just wrong. Do you intervene to correct your partner even though it means that they may lose face?

 YES

 NO

Your challenge causes greater embarrassment and confusion than you had expected. From your partner's reaction, you begin to think that there may well be reasons for the lie of which you were unaware. Do you persist in exposing the truth?

Another member of the party, it seems, is better informed than you had expected. They challenge the truth of what your partner has said. However, they are not well informed enough to expose the truth. Do you now chip in to help correct your partner?

 YES | **NO** *Question ends*

As you open your mouth, obviously intent on continuing in the same vein, you receive a weighty but in no way malicious kick in the ankle from your partner who embellishes it with a look that says 'There's something you don't know.' Do you still persist in trying to expose the truth?

NO | **YES** *Question ends*

Others join in the discussion against your partner, who is obviously embarrassed. Your partner turns to you for some moral support. Do you now correct your partner, or remain silent, rather than take their side?

QUESTION 22

You are in the countryside and have stopped to ask directions. The woman who answers the door is an ordinary, everyday, friendly sort of woman who invites you in for a cup of tea, which you accept. While you are talking to her and drinking the tea, you notice a vase in a corner. You happen to have a collector friend and know that the vase is worth about £400. You comment on the 'nice' vase. The woman laughingly replies, 'Oh, that old thing, it's always getting in the way and I never have liked it. If you like it, I'll gladly sell it to you.' She is not particularly well off but seems quite comfortable. She obviously does not know the true value of the vase. You happen to like the vase very much and can easily afford to offer a fair price based on what you know of its true value. You would like to buy it. Do you offer her a fair price based on what you know of its value?

 YES

 NO

You buy the vase. She is delighted that it was worth so much. Shortly after your return home, your collector friend comes round. On seeing the vase, they tell you that it is worth about £800. You could easily have afforded to buy it from the woman at a fair price based on this value. You have her phone number having parted on very friendly terms with her. Do you contact her to let her know its true value and offer to pay her more to reach a fair price on its true value?

Before you can say anything, there is a knock at the door. The woman answers it and returns with the local vicar. He is present as the woman asks you how much you are offering. Do you offer a fair price based on the true value of the vase?

 YES

| NO   *Question ends* |

The same situation, except that the collector friend tells you it's worth £20,000. You cannot afford to offer a fair price on this value. Do you phone the woman either to offer to return the vase or to suggest selling it and sharing the proceeds in some way?

 NO

| **YES**   *Question ends* |

The same situation, except that the visitor was not the vicar but another woman whom she introduces as a neighbour who has an antique shop. She tells the neighbour that you are just about to buy her old vase. The neighbour says hallo in a friendly manner. The woman who owns the vase then asks you how much you were offering. Do you offer her a fair price based on its true value?

QUESTION 23

You are at work when a colleague approaches you to join the union that represents your type of worker. You know that many of the other workers there already belong to this union. Do you join?

YES   **NO**

At a later date, after a secret ballot the union members in your place of work vote to strike over the 'unfair' dismissal of a colleague. They wish this person to be reinstated. You neither like nor dislike the person in question but believe their dismissal to be just. It is pointed out that should you fail to join the strike, you could lose your union membership. Do you join the strike?

YES | NO   *Question ends* |

The situation is the same, except that the person dismissed had been waging a secret hate campaign against you which had culminated in their assaulting you violently at work. There were no witnesses but your employers believed evidence strong enough to dismiss this person. Do you join the strike for their reinstatement rather than lose your union membership?

After some time, you realize that the union has negotiated better terms of employment for its members than you have received. You find that there is nothing you can do since the employers have managed this through differences of job descriptions, grades, etc. Do you now join the union?

NO | .YES   *Question ends* |

The management and the union have come to a closed-shop agreement. Non-union members will be offered redundancy pay if they do not wish to join the union. Yours would amount to three weeks' pay and you know that you would have difficulty finding another job as well paid. This is all perfectly legal under the laws at this particular time. Do you join the union?

QUESTION 24

You are helping your parents to sort out their packing as they are moving house. While moving a box, the lid comes off and some family papers fall out. As you repack them, your eyes fall upon your parents' marriage certificate. Seeing the date of their wedding, you realize that your brother was born six months afterwards. Your parents have never mentioned this, and have always claimed, you also realize, to have been married a year before they actually were. Do you now broach the subject with them rather than remaining silent?

 YES — — — — — — — — — — — — — — — **NO**

Your parents become very upset. After explaining to you the social situation at the time and their reasons, they ask you never to tell anyone, not even your brother. Do you refuse, or agree with the intention of informing your brother anyway, rather than agreeing to keep the secret with the intention of doing so?

The same situation, except that the dates show that your brother was born six months before your parents were married. Would you now broach the subject?

 YES | **NO** *Question ends* |

NO | **YES** *Question ends* |

. The same circumstances, except that you are helping your best friend's parents and the situation relates to your best friend. The parents see that you have noticed the marriage certificate and ask you not to tell their son, your best friend. Do you refuse to do this, either in words or spirit?

The same situation, except you discover that *you* were born six months before your parents were married. Would you now broach the subject?

QUESTION 25

You have been out for a drink with an old and very close friend. Your friend is of the same sex as you. Over a late-night coffee in the privacy of your home, your friend confides to you that they are gay. You had never suspected this nor has your friend ever made any approaches to you. Your friend explains that since you are an old friend, they felt that they should tell you as they would rather you found out that way rather than by accident. They also add that they have chosen, at the moment, not to tell any of your mutual friends. Normally, you meet this friend quite often socially, one-to-one, for drinks and trips to the cinema, etc. Do you continue to do so?

YES

You are having a drink with your friend one evening when some of your friend's gay friends come into the bar. You have never met them before. They are all openly and unashamedly gay. They are also of the same sex as you. You like them. They are friendly and amusing. Your friend and the others decide to go on elsewhere. It is a place that you know many of your workmates frequent. They are not gay and love to gossip. They do not know your gay friend. You are asked to go along with the group. You have nothing else planned for the evening. Do you go with them?

YES

| NO *Question ends* |

You are at your local sports club, having just played squash, or whatever is your wont, when you bump into your gay friend who has also been playing something there. You are in the changing rooms. Normally, you have a shower. Your friend is obviously going to. Do you proceed as normal and have a shower at the same time as they do?

NO

You later meet some close friends who are also close friends of your gay friend. You know that they are unaware of the fact and that several are so anti-gay that your gay friend would be socially ostracized by them if they knew. Do you tell them that you have found out that your friend is gay?

NO | YES *Question ends* |

One of the more perceptive, whom you also know loves spreading a bit of gossip, asks you quite pointedly, 'I notice you don't seem to be having much to do with X lately. Have you two fallen out about something?' Do you tell them the truth about your gay friend?

QUESTION 26

You are at a formal function. You bend over to pick up something and hear a slight rending at your rear. Clearly your trousers have come seriously adrift. A quick touch and you know that the seam has split down the centre. You will obviously have to go and make some emergency repairs in a quiet spot somewhere. You are with some friends. Do you own up as to why you are leaving the main room rather than make up some spurious excuse?

YES

The same situation except that you are not with any friends. You happen to be at a table with a group of people you don't know and who so far have not displayed much of a sense of humour. Do you still own up as to why you are leaving the main room?

YES | **NO**   *Question ends* |

You are again among the people you don't know, only this time it is a hot, sticky, summer's evening. For reasons of your own, possibly because it spoilt the line of your new trousers, you are not wearing any underwear. Do you still own up as to what has happened?

NO

One of your friends obviously has heard the noise as they ask one of the others what it was. You were just about to leave to effect emergency repairs. Do you now own up as to why you are leaving the main room?

NO | **YES**   *Question ends* |

You don't have anything with you, but you know one of the girls in the group always has some safety pins in her bag. Do you now say what has happened to anyone in your group?

QUESTION 27

You are at a party where you know most of the people. To your surprise, or otherwise, it soon becomes evident that virtually everybody there is smoking marijuana. You are offered some. Do you accept?

 YES

 NO

The same situation except that you are offered some speed. Do you accept?

The same situation, except some small bottles are being passed around and sniffed. Someone passes one to you and explains that a friend has just come back from America where this product can be bought freely in drugstores. It happens to contain amyl nitrite. Do you partake of this?

 YES | **NO**   *Question ends* |

The same situation except that cocaine is being used. You are offered a line. Do you accept?

 NO | **YES**   *Question ends* |

The same situation except that you are offered some pills that you recognize. Once, when you were ill, these had been prescribed for you by your doctor. They had cleared up your problem but you found that they had the pleasant side effect of making you good-humoured and relaxed. Do you partake of these?

QUESTION 28

The neighbour's cat has got into the habit of using a flower-bed in your garden as its lavatory. You're quite friendly with your neighbour, an elderly lady, and have mentioned this problem to her before. Although she's been quite sympathetic, she says she can't really do anything about it. A friend suggests that you put down some cat pepper. Do you do so?

YES   **NO**

The cat pepper seems to have no effect. The cat proceeds to happily use your flower-bed at its own convenience. Would you now throw a bucket of water over the cat the next time you saw it in your flower-bed?

The cat is an ungelded tom. Some very strong and unpleasant smells start to emanate from your flower-bed. Do you now put down some cat pepper?

NO   **YES** *Question ends*

The cat has taken to your flower-bed and often scrapes around at the surface. It has uprooted several of your favourite plants. Do you now put down some cat pepper?

YES   **NO** *Question ends*

The water barrage does not seem to deter the cat which still regularly returns. Would you now throw hard missiles at the cat the next time you had the opportunity?

QUESTION 29

You are taking your partner to a swanky restaurant with the intention of making a big impression. The restaurant is busy but you are well treated and the food is good. The waiter is attentive and courteous but at one point you have politely to ask him to remove a small caterpillar from your salad. The bill comes and you open your wallet – to your horror you realize that you have left your credit card at home. You have little cash on you and are unable to pay the bill. Do you cause a huge fuss because of the caterpillar and refuse to pay the bill?

 YES **NO**

YES — You stalk out haughtily without paying but your partner thinks you've behaved really boorishly. After a long and heated debate you tell the truth to your partner who promptly gives you some cash, tells you to go and apologize and pay the bill and storms off home. Do you still not pay the bill?

 YES | **NO** *Question ends* |

Your partner phones you in the morning and apologizes for being rather curt last night. Do you tell them that you did go back and pay the bill?

NO — The manager is upset but smilingly suggests that you do half an hour's washing-up to satisfy honour. You agree willingly but on stepping into the kitchen you see that it is incredibly messy and filthy. You spontaneously mutter something along the lines of 'My God! Have the health authorities seen this?' The manager promptly takes you to one side and says, 'Forget the washing-up and the bill. Consider the meal complimentary and I would be grateful if in return you say nothing to the health authorities.' Do you accept this offer?

 NO | **YES** *Question ends* |

The manager asks you to leave and pointedly remarks that you still owe the money for the meal. He asks that you return as soon as possible to settle the bill. Do you, however, omit to return and settle the bill?

QUESTION 30

You have agreed to look after your friends' flat while they are on holiday – and to feed their wretched cat. You will be living in. As an incentive, your friends have told you to help yourself to whatever is in the drinks cupboard while you are there. During the course of one evening, you have opened and consumed what you assumed to be a bottle of plonk. It is only the following day, when browsing through a magazine article on wine, that you realize you have imbibed a much-prized and extremely expensive bottle of Château-d'Yquem. Even if you could track down a bottle of the appropriate vintage, you could not afford to replace it. Your friends return from their holiday. Do you admit your mistake?

YES

Your friends admit that they had, in fact, forgotten all about the bottle in question. It had been a wedding present from a distant relative. They had not even appreciated the worth of the wine themselves. Do you nevertheless offer to supply an acceptable, expensive wine that you can afford?

YES | NO *Question ends*

Your friends will hear nothing of it and tell you to forget it. Do you still go ahead and buy them a bottle of wine or some other gift as a gesture of goodwill?

NO

A day after their return, your friends drop round to your place to thank you properly. They bring with them two bottles of rather good French wine, acquired on their holiday, as a gift for your help. Nothing is said about the bottle you drank. Do you now tell them about it?

NO | **YES** *Question ends*

A day or so later, they ring. They are looking for the bottle you drank. Apparently, they have had it some time and had just thought of giving it to a relative as a ruby wedding gift. They cannot remember where they had put it and thought you might have seen it while you were there. Do you now tell them that you drank the wine?

QUESTION 31

You are at an élite sporting event at the invitation of some business connection. You and the other guests are amicably sitting in a private box, eating and drinking and generally enjoying yourselves. One of the other guests, who seems quite affable, turns the conversation to athletics and begins to make disparaging remarks about a world record female athlete from the Soviet bloc, implying that this athlete has no right to compete in women's events, is of dubious sex, is ugly, etc., etc. The athlete in question holds several world records and has been routinely sex tested by the athletics board without controversy. Do you disagree with the man's opinions and say so?

 YES

 NO

He continues on the theme of women in sport, adding that he sees no reason why women tennis players should win equal prize money with the men as they only play three sets and even the best woman player would not stand a chance against a man player way down the world rankings. Do you disagree with the man's opinions and say so?

The situation is the same, except that the discussion is the result of a chance encounter on holiday. You will never see or hear from these people again. You have nothing whatsoever to lose by expressing your views. After voicing his opinions, the man turns to you and adds, 'Don't you agree?' Do you now voice any disagreement with the man's views?

 YES | **NO** *Question ends* |

 NO | **YES** *Question ends* |

The same situation, except that it is your company hosting the event and the man expressing these opinions is a valued client, although you have not encountered him before. Your boss, knowing your opinions, looks nervously at you. Do you still speak up and disagree with the man?

You are still on holiday. The man continues on the theme of women, adding that they should be in the home raising children and that their place is most definitely not at work or on the sporting field. Once again, he asks you if you agree. Do you voice any disagreement with the man's views?

QUESTION 32

You are walking along the street. It is pleasant and you are in no particular hurry. Coming towards you is someone you recognize, but you cannot recall who they are, what their name is or where you met them. The person is the same sex as you. All you can be sure of is that you have met them before and that you did not dislike them. They have not seen you. As they draw nearer, they have still not noticed you. As you pass, do you greet them?

 YES   **NO**

They clearly do not recognize you and look puzzled by your greeting. You are still convinced that you know them from somewhere. Do you continue to talk to them in the hope of jogging their memory as to where you know them from?	They greet you by name as you pass and exclaim that it's good to see you again. You still cannot place them or recall their name. After a few tactful words of conversation, you have still gained no clues. Do you continue the conversation to elicit more information, one way or another, rather than proceeding on your way at the first convenient opportunity?

YES   **NO** Question ends

They still do not know you, nor can you place where you know them from. After apologizing, you go on your way. However, after a few steps, it suddenly comes to you. You remember their name, where you met them and how. They had reacted quite amicably when you approached them just now. Do you go back and approach them again?

YES   **NO** Question ends

Would you go back and approach them again if they had been unfriendly when you first greeted them a moment ago?

 NO   **YES** Question ends

The original situation is exactly the same, except that this time the other person is of the opposite sex and someone who you find attractive. Do you now greet them as they pass?

QUESTION 33

Your closest relative was involved in a tragic car accident a week ago. Since then, they have been in a coma on a life-support system. The doctors ask for your permission to turn the machine off as your relative is clinically brain-dead. Do you give permission for the machine to be turned off?

YES

While you were pondering the issue, a similar case comes on the news of a child coming round from a coma as the result of a tape recording of his friends' voices being played to him. You ask the doctors about this but they assure you that it will not happen in your relative's case. Do you give permission for the machine to be turned off?

YES

NO *Question ends*

As you stand beside the bedside about to tell the doctors of your decision, you think you see your relative's eyelids flicker. You are not certain. The doctors say it was probably your imagination but it could have been a nervous reaction which is not unknown in such cases and indicates nothing. Do you still give permission for the machine to be turned off?

NO

The doctors point out that 2,000 patients join the waiting list for kidney transplants every year in London alone. They tell you that your relative is dead but could give the gift of life to four others and the gift of sight to two more. They show you that your relative cannot breathe on their own without the machine. Do you now give your permission for the machine to be turned off?

NO

YES *Question ends*

In this instance, you have another relative who is on the waiting list for a kidney transplant. This relative, though not in your immediate family, is related to you and the comatose relative by blood and not by marriage. Do you now give your permission for the machine to be turned off?

QUESTION 34

You are driving home from work when you witness a road accident between two motorists. There is no doubt that one of them was in the wrong as far as you are concerned because you saw the whole thing. However, the driver who was at fault is out of the car, screaming and raging at the driver who was in the right. There is nobody else around. The two drivers involved are both middle-aged men. Do you stop your car and offer to be a witness?

YES	NO
You are about to give your name and address when the driver who is in the wrong threatens to attack you if you interfere. Do you still offer to be a witness?	In this instance, the driver receiving the tirade is a middle-aged woman. She is very and visibly upset. Although she was in the right, she is so upset that she is actually beginning to blame herself for the accident under the pressure from the other driver. Do you now stop and offer to act as a witness?

YES | **NO**   *Question ends* |

He does not make good his threat. However, you receive a letter in the post which threatens all manner of dreadful things to both you and your family. You receive a form from the insurance companies involved. Do you still continue to act as a truthful witness?

 NO | **YES**   *Question ends* |

One of the drivers must have noted your number as you drove off as you are contacted by the police who ask you to give a full account of what you saw and to act as a witness. Do you now do as they request?

QUESTION 35

You are travelling in the no-smoking compartment of a train. There is nobody else in the compartment. The train stops. Just before it pulls out, another passenger opens the door to your compartment and hops hurriedly in – a perfectly average middle-aged man. He settles down in the corner, starts reading a magazine and absently lights up a cigarette. Do you ask him to stop smoking?

YES   **NO**

YES column	NO column
The same situation, except that your fellow passenger, to your surprise, is a nun. Do you ask her to stop smoking?	The train continues on its way. The compartment becomes very stuffy and dry as the heating seems to be jammed on high. It is midwinter and much too cold to open the window. The smoke seems to have a mind of its own and continues to drift in your direction. Do you now ask the man to stop smoking?

YES |NO   *Question ends*|

In this instance, your fellow passenger who has absently lit the cigarette is a burly youth with short cropped hair. He is wearing a short-sleeved T-shirt which reveals some rather elegant tattoos on his arms. Do you ask him to stop smoking?

NO |YES *Question ends*|

The train rattles on. The man begins to nod off with the lit cigarette in his mouth. Do you now ask him to stop smoking?

QUESTION 36

You are working in a boring job simply because you have been unable to find any work that you find interesting and suits your qualifications. A friend tells you that you have a good chance of getting a job with her company. The nature of the job is ideal for you and is the type of work you would like to do. However, the company is a large pharmaceutical manufacturer known to carry out extensive tests on animals. Your job would not be involved with any animal experimentation. Do you apply for the job?

YES / NO

YES

During the job interview, you are asked if you have any objections to vivisection. You cannot tell whether your answer will influence the interviewer's decision. Do you say that you have no objections to vivisection?

YES | **NO** *Question ends*

You go to a party where news of your possible employment has leaked. Many of your friends are obviously shocked and try to talk you out of it. At the end of the party, someone you respect hands you a powerful anti-vivisection leaflet. It mentions the company you have applied to and details some harrowing and horrific experiments that they conduct on rabbits, monkeys, dogs and other animals. The next day, you receive a letter from the company. You have been offered the job. Do you accept it?

NO

During the following week at work, you are told that your department is being phased out. You will be laid off or given an alternative job elsewhere in the company. However, the only alternative work you are offered is a terrible job sorting through old files. Do you now apply for the job at the pharmaceutical company?

NO | **YES** *Question ends*

Your friend with the pharmaceutical company tells you that the vacancy is in a section of the company that actually deals with anti-vivisection material as the company seriously takes their arguments into consideration. The company then changes its practices, where it feels appropriate, or presents counter-arguments. Your friend also points out that you, and many of your friends, use this company's products, often unknowingly. Do you now apply for the job?

QUESTION 37

You are on holiday in a remote part of the world . . . very, very remote. You are captured by a group of particularly nasty local terrorists. You have never heard of them or their cause. There are other prisoners at their camp. The terrorists give you a large knife and order you to kill one of the other prisoners who is bound and unconscious. You are alone in the hut with the prisoner you must kill. There are five armed terrorists in the large and only doorway. There is no escape and no cover. The prisoner is of your nationality. If you kill them as the terrorists order, you will be set free. You have already seen them keep this bargain with another prisoner. If you refuse, or try in any way to attack or deceive the terrorists, you will immediately be shot dead on the spot. Do you kill the bound and helpless prisoner?

 YES

 NO

Again, you are in the hut with the bound, unconscious prisoner. However, the terrorists order you to torture them slowly and hideously so that they die a slow and agonizing death. If you follow their orders, you will be freed. If you refuse, or try in any way to attack or deceive the terrorists, or should the victim die too quickly, you will be tortured to death in the same way. Do you torture the prisoner to death as the terrorists have ordered?

In this instance, the terrorists will not kill you if you refuse. Instead, they will execute two other prisoners of your nationality. Do you now kill the bound, unconscious prisoner as they have ordered?

 YES | **NO** *Question ends* |

In this instance, if you refuse to torture the prisoner to death, you will simply be shot dead on the spot. Do you still torture the prisoner to death as the terrorists have ordered?

 NO | **YES** *Question ends* |

In this instance, the terrorists will kill you if you refuse. However, they will not just shoot you. You are assured that you will be tortured slowly and agonizingly to death. Do you now kill the prisoner as they have ordered?

QUESTION 38

You have lost your job and are having some difficulty in finding another. You are quite hard pressed. A job comes your way that is ideal for your abilities and interests. However, it is with an organization that has a specific religious orientation or function. It is a religion of which you are not, and never have been, a practising member. It is, however, one of the principal religions and not some obscure cult. Being a member of the religion is not a prerequisite of the job, but during the interview you are asked whether you are a member of the religion. It is not a religion with whose doctrines you are familiar but you know that the job you are trying for will never involve any aspects of the religion. Do you tell the truth and say that you are not a member of that religion?

 YES　　　　　　　　　　　　　　 **NO**

The same situation except that it is a religion that you are familiar with, either having once practised it yourself or you have a very close friend who is a practising member. You could quite easily cope with any aspects of the job conditions that might involve the religion. Do you still tell the truth and say that you are not a practising member of the religion?

 YES　　| **NO**　 *Question ends* |

The same situation, in that you are familiar with the religion, except that it becomes clear during the interview that, although being a member of the religion is not a requirement of the job, the interviewer is so biased that you can see that they will only give the job to a member of their religion. When they ask if you are a member, do you still tell the truth?

You get the job and after a few weeks you are getting on very well with both the job and the other members of staff. An important religious festival is approaching. The staff will all have the day off. However, all members of staff will be going to a place of worship together. Since they believe you to be a member, you are expected to go. If you don't, you will be the only 'practising' member not to attend. Do you concoct some excuse rather than attend?

NO　　　| **YES** *Question ends* |

The religion is of a type that forbids certain foods. One lunchtime in a hurry you buy some sandwiches which contain a forbidden 'food' mixed in them. You have a lot of work on and take the sandwiches back to the office with you. A practising member of the religion is there. They have not had a chance to get anything to eat and ask if they can have one of your sandwiches. Since they have never tasted the ingredient in your sandwich, you know they will not recognize its presence. Do you make up some reason why they can't have one of your sandwiches rather than tell the truth, or allow them to unwittingly eat something that you know is against their religion?

QUESTION 39

You have been looking for a house for many months. At last you find one that would suit you at the right price. It is the right size and has a pretty garden, a pleasant interior and a good aspect. However, when you return for your second visit, you discover that although the house is in a quiet street, it is in the middle of a predominantly ethnic community who are of a different colour from you. Do you continue to pursue the purchase of the house?

YES   **NO**

You speak to a friend who used to live in the area and she tells you that more and more members of the particular ethnic group are moving into the area and that the people of your colour are moving out. However, there is no animosity, the area is pleasant and most people are friendly towards each other. House prices in the area are appreciating normally. Do you still pursue the purchase?

YES   NO   *Question ends*

The situation is the same except the two groups are not friendly towards each other. There is nothing openly hostile, but there is resentment. Do you still pursue the purchase?

The same situation except the area is split roughly fifty-fifty between the ethnic group and people of your colour. Neither group is predominantly moving into or out of the area, which has always had roughly the same mix with no problems. House prices in the area are appreciating normally. Do you pursue the purchase of the house?

NO   YES   *Question ends*

You hear that people of your colour are on the increase in the area and that the ethnic group is gradually moving away. There is at the moment a slight majority of people of your type. House prices in the area are appreciating normally. Do you pursue the purchase of the house?

QUESTION 40

Where you work, you are in charge of one section. You have others working under you. Your bosses decide that there should be an intermediate post in your section. This means a small promotion and pay rise for somebody. There are two people who are perfect for this new post. Both are equally good at their jobs, work equally hard, etc. They are equal in all respects. They are so good, that if either of them left they would be almost impossible to replace. However, one treats their work almost like a vocation. They love doing it and are always happy. They never complain to you about anything or ask for anything. The other is the opposite, in that they continually ask you for better pay. They have complained to you so much that you just want some peace and quiet from them. They have even intimated that if they don't get a rise soon, they may well leave. You now have the opportunity to shut them up. Do you give them the promotion and pay rise, remembering that both are ideally suited for the new post?

 YES　　　　　　　　　　　 **NO**

The same situation, except that the quiet, uncomplaining, happy-go-lucky one has been overlooked for just these reasons before . . . when you were promoted! At that time, you even thought that they were better suited but because everybody knew that they would never kick up a fuss, you got the promotion. Do you still give the post to the one who complains?	Before you've announced your decision, the squeaky wheel comes to see you. Once again, they complain about their pay and ask for a rise. You judge by their demeanour that they may have heard a rumour that there is one in the offing. You even spot them surreptitiously scanning the job ads in some magazines. Do you now give them the new post and pay rise?

 YES　　|　**NO**　*Question ends*　　 **NO**　　|　**YES**　*Question ends*

The squeaky wheel is happy. However, the uncomplaining one does not seem to be. Although they say nothing, they seem depressed and have lost interest in their work. Their work deteriorates dramatically to the point where their job could be in jeopardy. They respond to nothing. You get a directive from your bosses. The company has problems and you must lay off someone from your department. The uncomplaining one is now your worst worker. Do you lay them off?	You're just about to give your decision when the squeaky wheel returns to say that they are handing in their notice. They have found a new job for slightly better pay – though not as much as the new post would entail. Remembering that if either of the two left they would be almost impossible to replace adequately, do you now offer this one the new post and pay rise?

QUESTION 41

You hire a car for a weekend. While driving it over some bumpy ground, you hear an ominous grinding sound from underneath as you hit something. It seems OK, however, and you take the car back with no signs of damage. You were covered on the hire company's insurance but are eligible for the first £25 of any repairs. Do you tell them about the incident on the bumpy ground?

 YES

 NO

YES — You have hired a car abroad while on holiday when the same thing happens. From what you can tell of the hire agreement, you are not insured. Do you tell them of the incident on the bumpy ground when you return the car?

As you are leaving the car-hire firm, a good friend of yours arrives to pick up a hire car for a week. While you are talking, he is told that his car is ready. To your surprise, you see that it is the one you have just returned and your friend recognizes as much. The assistant tells your friend that it is the only one available. You have no chance to tell your friend of the bump, as the car-hire assistant is there all the time. Your friend is in a hurry and will drive off in the car unless you say something. Do you now tell the car hire firm about the incident?

 YES · | **NO** *Question ends* |

You have returned home from the holiday. Not long after, you receive a bill for £300, or its equivalent, from the foreign car hire firm for repairs to the car for the damage you caused. The firm has no links in this country. A friend in the know tells you that the bill and the damage quoted are reasonable and likely from your account of the incident. However, the bill will make a large hole in your finances. You can just pay it but it will leave you very short for at least four months. There is nothing the company can do to make you, but do you pay the bill?

 NO | **YES** *Question ends* |

The next time you see your friend, he is not too happy. The hire car broke down, it cost him £25 towards the repairs, and worse than that, it ruined his week away. He tells you that what he can't understand is that the hire company says he must have damaged the underside of the car when driving over some rough ground or up a kerb. However, he had done no such thing. He asks you if you had any trouble with the car while you had it for the weekend. Do you tell him the truth?

QUESTION 42

You once had an extremely good friend who was rather eccentric, though not in a bad way. You shared a flat with them. You haven't seen or heard from them for a few years. Then, all of a sudden, there they are on the front page of a newspaper. You read that they were trekking around the world. Somehow they were in an accident at sea and survived months in a small boat. They stayed alive by cannibalizing another survivor of the accident who later died. Your old friend also saw others eaten alive by sharks and had such a traumatic time that, when found, your friend was alive, just, but had completely lost their mind. They are now convalescing in a psychiatric institution. However, you are tracked down as the ex-flatmate by two newspapers. One is a popular newspaper that offers you £5,000 for your story. They wish to do a sensational story along the lines of 'I Lived With The Mad Cannibal'. The other is a more sober publication that offers £1,000. They wish to do a serious piece examining how a normal person can be reduced virtually to animal behaviour by tragic circumstances. Do you sell your story to either publication?

 YES

 NO

Do you sell your story to the highest bidder?

 YES | NO   *Question ends* |

The same situation, except that the person involved is your former lover. The highest bidder wants you to detail your sex life with that person to run a story of the 'Sex Secrets Of The Mad Cannibal' ilk. You are offered £10,000 for this. The more sober publication still wishes to run a story along its original line and is offering £5,000. Do you still sell to the highest bidder?

The same situation, except the person involved is not a friend of yours. You did share a flat with them but you couldn't stand them. Now do you sell your story?

 NO | YES   *Question ends* |

In this instance, although you shared a flat with the person, you don't even know them or anything about them. They were there for two weeks only, were always out, and only slept in the flat once in that period when you happened to be away. You only ever laid eyes on them once for about ten minutes. The popular paper is still willing to pay you £5,000 just to use your name and the 'I Lived With The Mad Cannibal' tag. They'll make up the rest. Do you now accept their payment?

QUESTION 43

You catch two young boys aged about nine or ten who have been throwing stones at your windows and nearly broke one. You recognize one of the children and know where they live although you do not know the parents. Do you warn the children rather than seek out their parents?

 YES

 NO

In this instance, this is not the first time that your windows have been the targets for missiles, although you have no means of knowing who was responsible before. Do you still just warn the children?

The children are clearly terrified that you have caught them. They apologize profusely and immediately offer to do any odd job you want done in recompense. Do you now just warn them?

 YES

| NO   *Question ends* |

 NO

| YES   *Question ends* |

As it happens, you have already warned these two boys before for tipping over your dustbin. Do you still just warn them again?

The children become more terrified as they realize that you will tell their parents. One of them almost begs you not to, saying that their father will only beat them again. He rolls up his sleeve and shows you some dark bruises where he has clearly been punched. Do you now just warn them?

YES

| NO   *Question ends* |

In this instance, nobody has thrown anything at your windows before nor have the boys tipped over your dustbin previously. However, in the original situation, they have actually just broken one of your windows when you catch them. Do you still just warn them rather than seek out their parents?

70

QUESTION 44

You have a relative who lives near one of the country's oldest nuclear power stations. While visiting them, they tell you what they claim is a true story. When the station was built, special equipment was designed to lower radioactive material into position. During installation, it was found that a coupling link was faulty. This meant that someone would have to descend a shaft and make the coupling by hand. This would expose them to dangerously high levels of radiation despite any protection. The authorities overcame the problem by offering a large sum of money to a mentally retarded person from your relative's village. That person later died. The Official Secrets Act and 'compensation' were used to hush up relatives and others in the know. You are the first person that your relative has told this to as they had no wish to do or say anything about it themselves. They confess that their conscience has now obliged them to tell someone. They would have no objection if you were to attempt to make the story known. Do you, anonymously or not, give the story to the press or other body that may publicize it?

YES

NO

Before you get the chance you notice slight irregularities in your mail and some odd noises on your telephone. Do you still try to get the story to the press or similar body to publicize it?

YES

| **NO** Question ends |

Once again, before you get the chance you receive a 'direct' warning. Some 'Special Branch' officers call to see you and in a roundabout way intimate that should your relative have told you anything and were you to repeat it you could both be in serious trouble. Do you still attempt to have the story publicized?

On a subsequent visit, your relative tells you that there have been many attempts by people to break into the power station. Any that the security police catch that they remotely suspect to be terrorists can be taken to Block A and summarily executed. No trial; no questions asked. Others can similarly be incarcerated in special prisons. Do you now attempt to get the stories publicized?

NO

| **YES** Question ends |

Your relative later tells you another story. A light, prefabricated office had been put up on the site of some buried radioactive waste from the early days of the station. Its location had somehow been unmarked and forgotten. Only after many of the typists, all locals, had been persistently ill was it realized: the hut was found to be badly contaminated and it and the waste were dumped, illegally, in the sea. Many of the typists have since died of or developed cancer. The dates and ages on their gravestones indicate that something 'happened'. Once again, the Official Secrets Act and 'compensation' were used to hush up the incident. Do you now attempt to get the stories publicized?

QUESTION 45

A long way from your home town, but still in the UK, you receive a parking ticket for illegal parking. You are not broke and can easily afford to pay the £12 fine, and you know full well that you were illegally parked. Do you promptly send the fine off in the post rather than just ignore it?

YES   **NO**

Before you do, a friend who has inside contacts tells you that only 50 per cent of cases involving non-payment are pursued by the authorities and that the authorities in this particular town are more lax than most. Do you still send the fine off in the post immediately?

YES | NO   *Question ends* |

In this instance, it was not your own car, but a hired one. Do you still send the fine off in the post immediately?

YES | NO   *Question ends* |

This time, not only was it a hire car, but you picked up the ticket abroad, in Italy. You had hired the car in France. Do you still send the fine off in the post immediately?

A friend tells you of the hassle they went through when a policeman arrived on the doorstep because of an unpaid fine. Do you now send the fine off in the post immediately?

NO | YES   *Question ends* |

You receive a letter in the post stating that if payment of the fine is not received by, in effect, the return of post, proceedings will be initiated. Do you now send the fine off in the post immediately?

QUESTION 46

You are on holiday, lying on a quiet beach in brilliant sunshine somewhere abroad. The whole scene is idyllic. There are a few other people lazing on the beach. You are just snoozing off when you hear some other people arrive. They settle down not too far from you. Shortly, you hear their portable cassette player boom loudly into life, vibrating with some music that you do not like. Everybody on the beach must be able to hear it. You look across to see a group of four teenagers: two boys and two girls. They are quite respectable-looking. On hearing them speak, you realize that they are also British. Do you say nothing rather than ask them to turn their music down or off?

YES

Somebody else comes over to them. However, this person does not speak English. In their own language, which you can just understand, he asks them to turn off the music. They, whether deliberately or not, fail to understand. The man repeats the request. Again they do not understand. The man is obviously getting angrier. Do you still remain silent rather than tell the teenagers what the man is asking?

YES | NO Question ends

Eventually, the man gets through to them. However, in the ensuing discussion one of the youngsters spots an English magazine in your bag. They then call to you in English asking you to support them and say that you don't mind the music. Do you still remain silent?

NO

A similar situation except that they are playing music that you happen to like very much. However, they are playing it loudly. Do you say nothing rather than ask them to turn it down or off?

NO | YES Question ends

In this instance, they are again playing music that you do not like but not loudly. The music is being played very quietly though it is loud enough to carry to where you are lying. The teenagers have obviously turned it as low as they can. Do you now say nothing rather than ask them to turn it off?

QUESTION 47

You are strolling in your local park one fine day. Suddenly, from another open space behind some bushes, some children come running. They are all of a different colour from you. They range in age from roughly six to ten. There are about seven of them. They are screaming and laughing in mock terror and looking back over their shoulders. Staggering behind them comes a man of your colour, about fifty years of age and blind drunk. So drunk, he is staggering in an erractic course towards the children. He is not particularly big or rough-looking. However, he is wielding a large stick and seems intent on pursuing the children for some reason. The children on their part seem to consider it a game and let him get fairly close before skittering off in various directions. The man is muttering and cursing, barely audibly. Do you proceed on your way rather than try to find out just what is going on?

YES

As you start on your way, you hear the man shout out that the little so-and-sos won't leave him in peace. He shouts at them to go away and to stop pestering him. They on their part laugh and jeer, throwing taunts at him to get him to chase them again. Do you still proceed on your way rather than speak to either party?

YES | NO *Question ends*

You've only taken a few steps when you hear a shout. On looking, you see that the children have begun to throw stones and anything else they can find at the man. He is too drunk to be able to dodge but none have as yet been on target. The man is getting angrier but cannot catch the children who continue to throw larger and larger hard objects at him. Do you still proceed on your way rather than intervene in any manner?

NO

The man curses the children for pestering and teasing him. However, he does so in foul and racist language. He waves the stick violently and staggers after them. The children for their part laugh and scream again but begin to throw stones quite viciously at the man. He is too drunk to dodge but none are on target as yet. Do you now continue on your way rather than speak to one or other of the parties involved?

NO | YES *Question ends*

The man is still shouting obscene racist remarks. The children are throwing stones. Do you approach and speak to the children first?

QUESTION 48

You are going back in time . . . The miners' strike is on. It has been going for some time. You are on your way to somewhere near where you live. You pass two striking miners who have come to your town. They are standing peaceably on the pavement holding buckets. There are stickers asking for money to help feed the families of striking miners. You are not broke. Do you put any money in their bucket?

 YES   **NO**

They are in the same spot every day, come rain or shine. You pass them each day. Do you put money in their bucket every day that you can afford it?

 YES | **NO**   *Question ends* |

One day they are not there. You hear in a local shop that several people complained about them and that the police moved them on under threat of arrest. You hear that they have now stationed themselves somewhere else. This is out of your way. To pass there would add fifteen minutes to your journey by foot. Do you go and find them to put money in their bucket?

As chance would have it, you visit some friends who happen to live near a coalfield. There is high unemployment and deprivation in the area that is all too obvious. One day, you and your friends happen to walk past the local pit on the edge of the town. You see a picket of two men at the main gate. In front of them is a large cardboard box. There is literally a queue of local people, some obviously shop owners, others equally obviously near-destitute. They are passing by dropping money, loaves of bread, tins of sardines, whatever they can into the box. Cars passing by stop and do the same. As you pass by, your friend does not put anything in the box. Do you?

 NO | **YES**   *Question ends* |

In this instance, your friend puts some money in the box – a £5 note. You know they have no sympathy with the strike, but equally you know that they must be familiar with the plight of the local people. Do you now put anything in the box?

QUESTION 49

You are trying to sell your flat. Over the years you have formed an amicable relationship with the rather conservative couple who live below you. They are upset that you are moving as you have always been extremely quiet and helpful. You know they are concerned about the type of people you might sell to. A young and rather outrageous punk shows great interest. He is a first-time buyer. Do you try to put him off?

YES
NO

YES | **NO**

The vendors of the house you hope to buy have contacted you to say that someone else is interested in their house and that they are in a better position to proceed. If you don't find a buyer for your flat soon you will lose the property you want. Do you still discourage your only potential buyer, the young punk?

YES | **NO** *Question ends*

You lose the house you had hoped to buy. You have not put in an offer on another property. This time an Iranian family, with three small children, is hoping to purchase your flat. Do you still take your neighbours' feelings into consideration and attempt to put them off?

He returns for a second viewing accompanied by his untidy, uncommunicative girlfriend and a large Alsatian. He tells you that he will offer the asking price. Your neighbours spot them as they leave. Later they call round and voice their doubts and worries about the punk. The neighbours then ask if they were interested. Do you tell them that they made a good offer which you might accept?

NO | **YES** *Question ends*

Your neighbours, who are obviously panicking, ask you round for a drink. They tell you that the wife's elderly mother is coming to live with them. They explain that this is another reason why they are so concerned about possible disturbing noise and anti-social behaviour coming from the flat above. Do you decide to wait a bit longer and not accept the young man's offer?

QUESTION 50

You are just entering a local school fête when you bump into an acquaintance, whom you have never particularly liked, about to enter the fête by themselves. Perhaps they are joining friends there. On their back some unkind joker has pinned a note which reads in big, bright letters 'Kick Me'. Do you tell them about the notice?

 YES

 NO

As you greet them, but before you can tell them about the note, they pointedly turn the other way, as though they have not noticed or heard you. Do you still warn them about the note on their back?

The person happens to be a fairly unpopular teacher at the school where the fête is being held. Do you now warn them about the sign on their back?

 YES

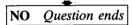 NO Question ends

 NO

YES Question ends

As you persist in trying to speak to them they turn and tell you to push off, or words to that effect. They obviously seem to be annoyed with you for some reason. You have still not been able to tell them about the sign. Do you still try to warn them?

As you enter the fête, you can see that there are many of the larger, more rough and unruly children of the area already there. You know that many of them will take the instruction on the sign literally. Do you now warn the person about the sign?

QUESTION 51

At a function organized by the company for which you work, the boss makes a speech in which he congratulates the staff for their hard work throughout the year. Near the conclusion, he says, in all seriousness, that 'The girls have worked like blacks, too.' You are standing near the back. Do you join in the applause at the end of the speech?

 YES   **NO**

You happen to be standing near another group of employees who are all female and white. You do not know any of them. Do you still applaud at the end of the speech?

 YES | **NO**   *Question ends* |

This time the group next to you happens to be black women. They pointedly refrain from applauding as the speech ends. Do you still applaud the speech?

If, earlier in the speech, the boss had unexpectedly announced a generous pay rise for everybody as reward for all the hard work, would you then applaud?

 NO | **YES**   *Question ends* |

This time, you happen to be at the front. As the applause starts, you can see that everybody else is applauding without exception. Do you now applaud?

QUESTION 52

You are on holiday in a remote part of the world . . . very, very remote. You are captured by a group of particularly nasty local terrorists. You have never heard of them or their cause. There are other prisoners at their camp. The terrorists give you a large knife and throw you into a hut with a bound and unconscious prisoner. There are five armed terrorists in the large and only doorway. There is no escape and no cover. The prisoner is of your nationality. The terrorists order you to cut out the prisoner's tongue and gouge out his eyes. If you do as they order, you will be set free. You have already seen them keep this bargain with another prisoner. If you refuse, or try in any way to attack or deceive the terrorists, you will immediately be shot dead on the spot. Do you do as the terrorists order?

 YES　　　　　　　　　 **NO**

In this instance, not only must you cut out the prisoner's tongue and gouge out their eyes, you must also cut off their hands and feet. Again, if you refuse, or try in any way to attack or deceive the terrorists, you will be shot dead on the spot. Do you do as the terrorists order?

In this instance, you must only gouge out the prisoner's eyes. Again, if you refuse or in any way try to attack or deceive the terrorists, you will be immediately shot dead on the spot. Do you do as the terrorists order?

 NO　　　| **YES**　*Question ends* |

 YES　　| NO　*Question ends* |

In this instance, your orders are the same as last time. However, the prisoner is your partner who was on holiday with you and was also captured. Do you submit your partner to the fate the terrorists have ordered?

In this instance, if you refuse to gouge out the prisoner's eyes, they will gouge out yours. They will not kill you. Again, you will be set free if you do as they order. Do you now gouge out the prisoner's eyes?

QUESTION 53

You are in the countryside and have stopped at a house to ask directions. The woman who answers the door is an ordinary, everyday, friendly sort of woman who invites you in for a cup of tea which you accept. While you are talking to her and drinking the tea, you notice a vase in a corner. You happen to have a collector friend and know that the vase is worth about £400. You comment on the 'nice' vase. The woman laughingly replies, 'Oh, that old thing, it's always getting in the way and I never have liked it. If you like it, I'll gladly give it to you for nothing.' She is not particularly well off and obviously does not know the true value of the vase. You don't happen to like the vase either. Do you accept the vase as a free gift there and then?

YES

The situation is the same, except that the woman is a relative of yours, an aunt whom you rarely see and happen to be visiting only because you were in the area. Do you accept the vase there and then as a free gift?

YES | **NO   *Question ends***

The news travels through the family grapevine quite fast. A close relative whom you see frequently and who also knows the collector comes to visit you. Not knowing that you know the true value of the vase, they tell you the value as they have seen it before. They suggest that since your aunt was unaware of its value, you could let her know, return the vase or sell it and give her a fair share of the profits. They are not accusing you of anything and think that you were totally unaware of its value. Do you keep the vase, or the money realized from selling it, rather than follow your close relative's suggestions or anything similar to them?

NO

She laughs and says, 'It's worth about £400, you know. I don't really need the money and I don't like the vase. You're really welcome to it if you want. It's not often I meet any new people out here, and I'd be glad for you to take it.' You have no need for the money either and you still don't particularly like the vase. Do you accept the gift?

NO | **YES   *Question ends***

She laughs again and goes over to a small cupboard. She returns with a small vase and says, 'I don't like this one either and I'm sure it's worth nothing like the other one, but I'd like you to have it if you like it. I don't have any relatives and it has been such a pleasure talking to you.' You really like this vase and have no idea of its value. Do you accept this gift?

QUESTION 54

You live near a college. You have a spare room and you are so short of cash that you must take in a summer student for six weeks to be able to make ends meet. You have no alternative. You contact the college and find that there are only two students still without accommodation. You meet them both. They are of the same European nationality, the same sex, equally affable, friendly, etc. In essence, they are identical in all respects *except* one is the same colour as you and the other is not. Do you toss a coin, or use some other random method, to decide who to rent the room to rather than choose yourself?

 YES   **NO**

In this instance, one is a coloured American and the other is a white Russian. Do you still toss the coin?

You have decided to choose. Do you choose the one that is a different colour from yourself?

 YES | NO · *Question ends* | **NO** | **YES**   *Question ends* |

In this instance, one is a white South African and the other is a coloured South African. Do you still toss a coin?

The same situation, except that both are the same colour as you. However, one is American and the other is Russian. Do you now toss a coin to decide?

 NO | **YES**   *Question ends* |

You have decided to choose. Do you choose the Russian?

QUESTION 55

You are out with a friend in the country following what was marked as a public footpath. You have a good map of the area with you. As you turn a bend in a wooded section of the path, you come to a fence with a gate across the path. The gate is locked but easy to climb. From the worn paint on the gate you can see that it has often been climbed. However, there is a large sign across the path on the other side of the gate saying 'Trespassers will be prosecuted'. You are out for a pleasant walk. You can get to where you were heading by other ways, but this would involve doubling back and walking about three extra miles. Do you continue on down the footpath?

YES

NO

You pass the sign to find that the path ahead is completely overgrown and almost indistinguishable. To all intents, it seems to stop some ten yards past the sign. Your map clearly shows a path that should leave the thicket shortly. The path is not overgrown with anything inconvenient such as brambles or nettles. Do you still carry on?

In this instance, the sign is rather old and the paint is peeling. The lock on the gate is caked in rust. Do you now continue along the path?

 NO   **YES**   *Question ends*

Just then, another walker appears coming the other way. They hop over the gate, nod a quick greeting and stroll on. Do you now continue along the path?

YES   NO   *Question ends*

As you approach the edges of the thicket, you hear gunfire. Ahead in a field you see a party of clay-pigeon shooters just beginning to practise their sport. You can see several crates and some are still sitting on the grass drinking what seems to be beer. The path runs across the field fifty yards in front of them. They are on a river bank so it would be impossible to pass behind them. Do you still carry on along the public footpath?

QUESTION 56

You are called for jury service. Sitting comfortably with the rest of the jury, you are shocked by the first case. There in front of you in the dock is a face from the past. Many, many years ago, you were madly in love with someone who was and always will be the great love of your life. While you were out of the country, the person in the dock stole your love away with charm and by telling lies about you. Then, they caused your ex-lover such pain and misery as to result in a tragic suicide. In short, there in the dock is the person who you have just cause to hate most in the world. The crime for which they are on trial could result in five to ten years' imprisonment. Although you have recognized the person in the dock – after all you have good reason to remember them – they do not recognize you. You know that any juror is bound to notify the foreman of the jury of any personal interest in the case and so step down from the jury. Do you notify the foreman?

YES

NO

The same situation, except the person in the dock is someone who once helped you financially. The money was sent your way by way of business through a mutual friend and came at a time when you were in desperate straits. The person in the dock did it as a favour for your mutual friend; you only found out the full story later and never had a chance to thank them in any way. Do you still notify the foreman of the jury?

During discussions in the jury room, it becomes obvious to you that the jury could well be split and that the verdict virtually depends on your vote. From the evidence presented, you would normally feel that the person on trial is not guilty. Do you vote 'not guilty'?

NO | **YES**   *Question ends* |

Your vote tips the scales. The verdict is guilty. You return to the courtroom. As you enter, you notice that the person in the dock looks twice at you. They have obviously recognized you but, equally obviously, cannot yet place you. As the jury sits down, the person is still glancing at you curiously. The foreman has not yet delivered the verdict. As far as you know, a jury verdict, once delivered, cannot be overturned by reason of your ineligibility. However, you will almost certainly be held in contempt of court once the defendant recalls exactly who you are, which it looks as though they will – although not until later. Do you now notify the foreman of your personal interest before the verdict is delivered?

YES | **NO**   *Question ends* |

The same as before, except the person in the dock is the person who once saved your child's life in a boating accident. You never knew their name and only saw them the once, but you remember them and have never had any chance to show any gratitude. Do you still tell the foreman of the jury of a personal interest?

QUESTION 57

You are on holiday on a Mediterranean island. After studying some local maps you set off by your own transport to spend the day on a quiet remote beach. When you arrive, you find that the beach is quite crowded, but not overly so. There is still plenty of room, though wherever you go there will be other people about thirty feet from you. The nearest other beach is a considerable journey away and would mean that you have wasted most of your day in travelling. On this beach, however, everybody is sunbathing nude. Do you stay here and sunbathe nude?

 YES   **NO**

The situation is the same, except the majority of the people are not sunbathing nude. You can see a short section of the beach where people are sunbathing nude. Do you now stay and sunbathe nude?

On another day, you reach this beach and it is nearly empty. You can see a few people about 100 yards away who are sunbathing nude. Do you sunbathe nude?

 YES | NO   *Question ends* |

 NO | YES   *Question ends* |

The same situation, except that you can see only one other person sunbathing nude. That person is the same sex as you. Do you also sunbathe nude?

You find another really secluded beach way off the beaten track. It is totally deserted. Would you now sunbathe nude?

QUESTION 58

You have received great hospitality as the house guest of some people you don't know very well. You are there due to a mutual friend. On the last morning, at breakfast, your hosts launch into a bitter tirade against what happens to be your particular political beliefs. Do you make your views known?

YES

NO

A fairly heated reply shows that your hosts have warmed to the subject and, most decidedly, cooled towards you. Do you continue to defend your views rather than try to smooth things over by acquiescing to your hosts' views?

The mutual friend who took you on the weekend knows your views. They speak up at this juncture, saying that they are sure that you will have something to say on this. Everybody looks to you; do you now express your views?

YES

NO   *Question ends*

NO

YES   *Question ends*

The same initial situation, except that your hosts have a swimming pool and a beautiful house in the country. You have enjoyed the weekend enormously and would like to go there again. Your hosts have invited you to come whenever you want and you had intended to take them up on their offer. When your hosts express their opinions at the breakfast table, do you speak up to defend your views?

Some time later, your mutual friend brings your ex-hosts to a party you are giving at your house. Your ex-host again expresses his views. Do you take the advantage of being on home ground, amid fellow sympathizers, to express your views now?

QUESTION 59

You and your brother are very close. However, you discover in later life that he is a petty criminal involved in small-scale larceny from offices and warehouses. You know that your brother would never hurt anyone. He is single and has always been very generous to both you and your parents. Do you tell the police about his criminal activities?

 YES

 NO

 The situation is the same, except that your brother is married. He and his wife have a young child. You get on well with his wife and she knows of his criminal activities. Do you inform the police of your brother's activities?

YES | **NO** *Question ends* |

You realize that several gifts given to you by your brother in the past were all probably stolen. These include some of your favourite clothes and some items that you cannot immediately afford to replace (such as stereo equipment). Do you also hand these in to the police?

Your brother has borrowed your car. When he returns it, he tells you he was involved in a minor accident and that the number on your car will probably be traced. He is worried that if he is reported as the driver in the incident, the police may fingerprint him and connect him with some warehouse robberies for which he could get several years' imprisonment. The offence was minor, your brother went through a red light but was seen by a policeman. He asks you to say you were driving. The police trace the car to you. Do you tell them it was your brother?

 NO | **YES** *Question ends* |

The proceedings take a nasty turn. Possibly because they suspect your brother is a criminal, the police are tarring you with the same brush and pushing for more charges than the offence seems to warrant. They have discovered that you were drinking in a pub, which is true but you have no witnesses to show that you walked home. You could lose your licence for three years, although your car is not essential to your job. Do you tell the police that it was your brother driving?

 NO | **YES** *Question ends* |

The same situation as before, except that your car is essential to your job. Without your licence, you will lose your job. Do you now tell the police that it was your brother?

QUESTION 60

A good friend tells you in all seriousness that at a séance they received a definite message from the 'other side' from someone who had recently died. You have always found this friend very reliable. Do you genuinely believe them rather than just merely humour them?

YES

Encouraged by your comments, your friend proceeds to describe the experience. They admit that the message was so vague that anyone could have dreamed it up, but they say that at the séance they had a clear *feeling* of communication. Do you still believe them?

YES | **NO** *Question ends*

As their description of the séance continues, it becomes clear that it was a rather amateur affair started by a few drunken friends for a laugh. Do you still believe your friend had a message from 'beyond'?

NO

In this instance, the friend telling you about the séance had previously pooh-poohed spiritualism. However, this experience has clearly convinced and converted them. Do you now believe their story?

NO | **YES** *Question ends*

Your friend goes on to describe the feelings and messages they received. They admit to being puzzled by one message that told them not to worry about a mutual friend, by name. Unbeknown to anyone except you, this particular friend is seriously ill. Do you now believe your friend's story of the séance?

QUESTION 61

You are in your smartest clothes as you have an important business lunch with a client. Having arrived early, you are relaxing outside the restaurant in the bright sunshine. Struggling towards you along the pavement is an old lady weighed down by heavy shopping. She looks very unsteady. It is a few minutes before the agreed time for your lunch. There is nobody else nearby. You are the closest person to the old lady. Do you offer to help her?

YES

You approach and offer your help. However, she seems a bit deaf and is obviously confused. Before you can say anything, she mistakes your intentions and begins to shout abuse and tries to hit you. This has attracted the attention of other people further away who are now watching. Do you persevere with your attempts to help the old lady?

YES   NO   *Question ends*

She becomes even more afraid of you and shouts abuse even louder and starts to hit you again. From the corner of your eye, you can see that the person with whom you are having the important business lunch has arrived and is among the observers of the scene. Do you still continue to try to help the old lady?

NO

She trips and falls sending her shopping flying all over the pavement. A few other people are within earshot and she is crying for help, although not injured. It is time for you to meet your important client inside. Do you now help the old lady?

NO   YES   *Question ends*

At this moment, your client arrives. They rush to help the old lady and have clearly not noticed you lounging nearby. You could easily pretend that you have just arrived, so do you now go over to help the old lady?

QUESTION 62

Recently, you have discovered that your teenage son is an alcoholic. When you make some enquiries, you find that there is a suitable NHS treatment centre in your area, but there is only one and it has a long waiting list. An acquaintance who has had experience of a similar problem recommends you to a private clinic which you can just about afford. Do you book your son into the private clinic?

YES

NO

He is doing well and the doctors tell you about a marvellously beneficial holiday that they organize for their patients in the South of France. It is expensive and exclusive but has been proved to help the cure. You can just afford it but it would mean cancelling your own holiday. Do you send your son on this treatment holiday?

After a long wait, your son receives counselling at the NHS clinic. However, you notice that he is becoming influenced by a group of rather destructive teenagers who are not only alcoholics but also drug addicts. Do you now switch over to the private clinic?

NO   **YES**   *Question ends*

YES   NO   *Question ends*

Your son returns and his treatment has been a complete success. You are impressed. The huge bill arrives, accompanied by a form offering very reasonable terms for private medical insurance for your family. Do you take out the insurance?

He doesn't seem to be making any progress and could even be deteriorating. While cleaning his room, you discover a small tin containing a packet of white powder which turns out to be heroin. Do you now switch over to the private clinic?

QUESTION 63

Your mother has spent a great deal of time and effort on knitting a jumper as a surprise gift for your birthday. You had no knowledge of this. When she gives it to you and you see it for the first time, you absolutely loathe it. It is exactly the sort of thing that you would not be seen dead in. Do you, however politely and tactfully, say so?

YES

NO

She is obviously upset although the issue blows over quite quickly. Shortly afterwards, she is coming to visit you. It is a chilly day, the sort of day on which you would wear a jumper. For her visit, do you wear a jumper that you like rather than the one she knitted you?

Your mother is pleased that you like it, saying that she was sure that it would suit you. She comes to visit shortly afterwards, it is a chilly day, the sort of day on which you would normally wear a jumper. Do you wear one that you actually like for your mother's visit rather than the one she knitted you?

 YES

| NO   *Question ends* |

Your front drains are blocked. You can easily clear them but it is a particularly dirty job, guaranteed to cover your clothes in filth. It is chilly and the only suitable item you have that you are not too bothered about is your mother's jumper. You are in the middle of clearing the drains and covered in muck when your mother turns up out of the blue. She is obviously disconcerted to see you getting the jumper into such a state. Do you, however politely and tactfully, tell her the truth rather than concoct some plausible reason, such as you had worn it quite a lot and it needed washing anyway?

NO

| YES   *Question ends* |

Because your mother sees you wearing the jumper now and again when she visits, she says that she plans to knit you another in the same style but a different colour. Do you, however politely and tactfully, now speak up?

90 ·

QUESTION 64

You're on a fairly long train journey and have nothing to occupy your time, other than gazing idly out of the window. The countryside is flat and boring. The person next to you in the silent but crowded compartment is reading today's paper which you haven't seen. They are not someone whom you wish to talk to. Do you surreptitiously read their paper over their shoulder?

YES   **NO**

The reader realizes what you are doing and irritatedly turns the page making unnecessarily heavy weather of the operation. Once they have settled down again, do you start to read it surreptitiously again?

YES | **NO**   *Question ends* |

You are reading an interesting article when the reader grumpily turns to you and mutters, 'Can't you afford your own?' They then turn a bit so that you'd have to lean forward slightly to continue reading. Do you still continue to try to read their paper?

As they turn the page, you notice that the paper is the local from your home town, although you are at the moment far from home. The person is still not someone whom you would wish to engage in conversation. Do you now try to read the paper surreptitiously?

NO | **YES**   *Question ends* |

As they turn the next page, a small headline catches your eye. It contains your family name. Do you now try to read the paper?

QUESTION 65

You are single. Someone you have met a few times through acquaintances asks you to go out with them one evening. It is obvious that they are attracted to you. You are not the least bit attracted to them although you can tolerate their presence quite happily. However, they are very well off. You know them well enough, and their intentions, to know that if you were to tell them that you did not find them attractive they would cease to invite you out. They invite you to a very expensive restaurant at their expense. It is somewhere that you have always wanted to go. Do you accept their invitation?

 YES

 NO

You enjoy the meal, if not their attentions and company. During the course of the meal, they tell you they have tickets for a show in a few days' time. It is a show you want to see but tickets are incredibly expensive and like gold-dust. You know that if you tell the person that you do not find them attractive, the invitation will be withdrawn. Do you go to the show with them?

 YES | **NO** *Question ends* |

Your birthday is near. You know that the person intends to buy you a very expensive gift as they believe that you are interested in them. You are not. To say so would mean no present. Do you keep quiet until after your birthday at least?

There is a show on that you would dearly love to see. However, tickets are ludicrously expensive and impossible to get. This person contacts you. They have two tickets and would like you to go with them. They obviously hope to curry your favour. Do you accept the invitation?

 NO | **YES** *Question ends* |

You happen to bump into this person a few more times socially and actually grow to like them quite a bit. So much so that you would accept an invitation to go out with them. However, you are currently seeing someone whom you like equally. This person is broke although they are great fun. The one with the money asks you out again. You know that if you accept, your poorer partner will take umbrage and disappear from your life. You like them both equally as people. Do you now accept the invitation?

QUESTION 66

Christmas is coming, the geese are getting fat but you're rushing around trying to buy presents. There are only a few more days left and you still have several to buy. You will be spending Christmas at the home of some close friends. They have an eight-year-old son. You need to buy him a present. You have asked what he wants and have been told that what he is asking for is a toy gun, 'A Magnum just like Dirty Harry has.' Your friends have no objection to this. Do you choose to buy the toy gun for the boy?

 YES

 NO

This time, it is the boy himself who has told you that the gun is what he really, really wants more than anything. You do not know whether the parents approve of toy weapons. Do you still buy the boy the gun?

 YES | **NO   Question ends** |

Once again, it is the boy who has told you that he wants the gun, but this time you know that the parents disapprove of toy weapons and would never buy one for the child themselves. Do you still choose to buy the boy the toy gun?

The boy had also said that there was a game that he wanted. You find the game to discover that it is a war game with little nuclear missiles. Time is running out, you have only one more day left and you have so far seen nothing else that you thought would be suitable. Do you now buy the toy gun for the boy?

 NO | **YES   Question ends** |

It is now Christmas Eve. Just a few more shopping hours left. You are desperate. Everything worth-while seems to have disappeared from the shops. All you can find is the toy gun the boy wants and a road safety game that looks rather dreary and uninspired. There is no time left to look any further. Do you now buy the toy gun?

QUESTION 67

You have been to a party with your partner. Later, you are both reclining on the sofa at home. Your partner turns towards you, you can see an amorous look in their eye. You also are in the mood. They lean towards you tenderly. Their lips move towards yours. As they move closer . . . you realize that their breath smells overpoweringly of stale cabbage. Heaven knows what they were eating at the party! Do you say nothing rather than spoil the mood by pointing this out?

YES

Your partner seems intent on a long smoochy seduction. However, their breath is foul at the moment. You can hardly bear to kiss them for more than a moment at a time. However, you are still feeling amorous. Do you continue the seduction, regardless of whether you tolerate kissing them or avoid it, rather than say anything and risk spoiling the mood?

 YES | NO · *Question ends* |

For some reason, your partner seems in the mood for long-drawn-out passionate kisses. You are now finding this off-putting and are feeling less and less amorous by the minute. Do you still say nothing about their breath?

NO

Before you do so, you realize what it was that they ate at the party. You know from a previous experience that no amount of mouthwash or anything else will remove the smell from their breath until it wears off naturally, some time tomorrow. Do you now say nothing rather than risk spoiling the mood?

 NO | YES *Question ends* |

In this instance, your partner's breath still smells but you know that whatever it was that they have eaten, you have also eaten it and that your breath smells just the same as well, although you are not aware of it. Do you now say nothing about your partner's breath?

QUESTION 68

You have an old car that has given you years of good service but is now starting to give trouble and is proving expensive to keep on the road because of the repairs required. However, it still has an MOT certificate with a few months to run. The floor of the car is seriously rusty and will eventually give way in places.

You decide to sell the car privately and a rather dreamy buyer answers your advertisement. They apparently know nothing about cars and are looking for a cheap runabout. They don't inspect the car properly and are prepared to pay your asking price. Do you warn them about the condition of the car?

YES

Before you get round to mentioning the problems, the buyer makes a few casual remarks that indicate that they have, in fact, much more technical knowledge about cars than you had supposed. They are not boastful or objectionable in any way, but they do seem to be quite an expert. Do you still tell them about the condition of the car?

YES | NO   *Question ends* |

This time, others had already answered your advertisement and turned the car down. This is your only chance to sell. Do you still warn of the condition of the car?

NO

Recently, the brakes have played up a bit. You have a feeling that the rust may be affecting the brake pipes and that they might actually fail at some future time unless preventative action is taken. Now do you warn the buyer about the car's condition?

NO | YES   *Question ends* |

As you are concluding the deal, the buyer tells you that they were involved in a very serious accident a few years back. They were badly injured but now wish to buy a cheap car just to get a bit of confidence back on the road. Do you now warn them of the condition of the car?

QUESTION 69

One way or another you have ended up on holiday with a group of friends. They are not close friends, more acquaintances. However, you all get on reasonably well and are enjoying yourselves. After a few days it becomes evident that one of the group has short arms and long pockets. Whenever rounds of drinks are bought or group bills paid, this person somehow seems always to avoid paying. However, nobody else in the group seems willing to raise this issue with them though they have all noticed. Do you say anything to this person about their meanness?

YES

They apologize and say that it was not intentional. They then make an effort over the next few days to be seen to be paying their share. Then they slip back into their old ways again. The next time that there is a joint bill to be paid, do you, tactfully or otherwise, suggest or indicate that it is this person's turn to pay?

YES | NO *Question ends* |

As it turns out, the person claims not to have their money with them. They have forgotten it! However, you have all befriended a group of Liverpudlians in the meantime. They have passed comment on the person's unwillingness to pay and hatch a plan. They suggest that you all meet in a bar where they know the barman who will put the entire evening's drinks on to one bill. Your group slips out gradually leaving them with the stingy one. They will then leave *en masse* telling the barman that the tightwad will pay. If they've forgotten their money again, they'll be in a right fix. You don't even know if the person would have enough to settle a bill like that. Do you agree to go along with the plan?

NO

They continue to avoid paying for anything whenever possible. One evening, you are all in a restaurant. The bill comes. Do you, tactfully or otherwise, suggest to the person that it is their turn to pay?

NO | YES *Question ends* |

In this instance, the tightwad is a closer acquaintance of yours than of anyone else's. They are all growing annoyed with this person's behaviour. It is beginning to spill off on to you. Everybody evidently feels, though nobody has said so, that it is up to you to say something. Do you now confront the person about their meanness?

QUESTION 70

You are in a rush to catch your train and have no time to buy a ticket. As it is, you only just catch the train. When you reach your destination, there seems to be no check on tickets. You know the fare should be £3, which you have on you and can easily afford. Do you try to pay for your ticket?

YES **NO**

There does not seem to be anyone around who is at all interested in collecting your fare. After a few minutes you have still not found anyone. You are not in a hurry and must wait for a cab anyway. Do you still try to pay your fare?

As you pass through the barrier, you see an honesty box. It is securely protected and bears a notice for tickets and unpaid fares to be placed in the slot at the top. There is nobody else around. Do you pay your fare?

 YES | **NO** Question ends | **NO** | **YES** Question ends

Just then there is a shout from the other platform. A railwayman shouts that he'll be over in a minute and disappears into a room where you can hear a telephone ringing. The ringing stops. After five minutes the man has still not re-emerged. Do you still try to pay your fare?

This time there is a ticket inspector on duty. However, he is occupied at the barrier with another passenger. You could sneak through without attracting his attention. Do you try to pay your fare?

QUESTION 71 (female)

You have had a depressing day and you return home in need of cheering up. The bell rings and you open the door to find your next-door neighbour holding a large and beautiful bunch of flowers. Interflora called while you were out and she took them in for you. When she has gone, you open the card attached to the flowers to discover that the flowers have been delivered to you in error. You can see that they were meant for someone who happens to live in a street with a similar name to your street. The delivery person obviously misread the address. This street is about twenty minutes away. The message on the card simply reads 'With love from Gerry'. Do you keep the flowers rather than try to get them to the rightful recipient?

 YES   **NO**

In this instance, the card reads, 'Happy Birthday with all my love and best wishes, Gerry'. Would you still keep the flowers?

 YES | NO   *Question ends* |

The next day, you are walking down the road when you bump into an acquaintance. She tells you that a disabled woman for whom she shops is extremely upset because her only son, Gerry, forgot her birthday. Do you still keep the flowers?

Just as you are preparing to return the flowers, the door-bell rings again. It is a friend of yours who has always been very successful with men; you have sometimes felt overshadowed by her 'romantic' life. She is immediately impressed by the splendid bunch of flowers. She promptly offers to help you arrange them and makes to unwrap them. Do you allow her to do so?

 NO | YES   *Question ends* |

The same situation, except today is St Valentine's Day. There was no message with the flowers. You have not received any other cards or flowers. Do you now allow your friend to unwrap and arrange the flowers, or continue to give the impression that they are yours, rather than admit that they were not for you?

QUESTION 72

There is a large company whose products you use regularly and find extremely good. You learn that the company makes horrific experiments on dogs in its testing. There are alternative products from other companies who do not make such experiments, but none are as good or as reasonably priced. Do you continue to buy the company's products?

 YES   **NO**

In this instance, the company does not experiment on dogs. You learn that it conducts horrific experiments on the eyes of live rabbits. Do you still continue to buy the company's products?

 YES |NO   *Question ends*|

In this instance, the company does not experiment on rabbits. Instead it uses dead human embryos from abortions. Do you still continue to buy its products?

Due to public pressure, the company changes its policy. It experiments now only on laboratory-bred rats. Would you now buy its products?

 NO |YES   *Question ends*|

The company still only experiments on these rats. However, there is no alternative to the product. It happens to be your favourite but it is not an essential. You can live without it. Do you now buy the company's product rather than go without?

QUESTION 73

You have recently been in contact with chicken pox. You begin to feel as though you're sickening for something, but you don't feel too bad. However, this is the day before a party that you have been looking forward to for months. The party is being thrown by some very close friends of yours in honour of some other friends who now live abroad. They will be there and it will be your only chance to see them while they are in this country. Do you go to the party?

YES

NO

Just before you leave for the party, the hostess phones you to ask if you could bring something with you that she wants to borrow. In conversation, you learn that her children have only just recovered from a particularly nasty form of flu which has left them weak and the whole family worn out. So worn out, in fact, that the party was nearly called off. Do you still go to the party?

In talking to a friend, you learn that someone you find very attractive but have never yet had the chance to meet will be at the party. Do you now decide to go to the party?

YES

NO   *Question ends*

The same situation, except that there will be nobody special at the party. There will only be friends that you see quite often, and some others whom you don't know. Do you still go to the party?

NO

YES   *Question ends*

You also learn that another acquaintance will be there. This person happens to owe you £50, which you could do with at the moment. You hear that they will be going abroad to work and leave the day after the party. This will be your last chance for some time to get the money back. Do you now go to the party?

QUESTION 74

You are playing the Truth Game with the people in this room. The Truth Game is very simple, and very nasty. There is one rule. All questions must be answered truthfully. Anyone can ask anyone else any question. Someone asks you to tell what you have done in your life that you are most ashamed of. Do you answer truthfully rather than lie or decline to answer?

 YES

 NO

You are asked to say who in the room, other than your partner, you find the most sexually attractive. Do you answer truthfully rather than lie or decline to answer?

You are asked to relate the most embarrassing thing that has ever happened to you. Do you answer truthfully rather than lie or decline to answer?

 YES

| NO   *Question ends* |

 NO

| **YES**   *Question ends* |

You are asked to relate your most erotic experience. Do you answer truthfully rather than lie or decline to answer?

You are asked to reveal a secret, any secret, about yourself that you have never before told anyone in the room. Do you answer truthfully rather than lie or decline to answer?

QUESTION 75

You are driving along a quiet country road late at night. It is dark and overcast. You round a bend. Ahead you can see an old Austin Cambridge pulled off the road. From what you can make out in the darkness, there seems to be someone crouched on the far side of the car by the wheel. It would appear that the driver has a flat tyre. Do you stop and offer any help?

 YES   **NO**

As you slow down, the driver rises and steps into the road to flag you down. In your headlights, you can see that it is a young man, and that there is another young man seated in their car. The young man flagging you down appears to be respectably dressed. Do you still stop and offer help?

 YES | **NO**   *Question ends* |

The driver explains that something seems to be wrong with his front axle and asks if you could give him and his companion a lift to the next town, about fifteen miles away. It happens to be where you are going. Do you give them a lift?

As you approach, the figure crouched by the wheel rises and steps into the road. It is a respectably dressed young man. He flags you down. There is nobody else in his car. Do you now stop and offer any help?

 NO | **YES**   *Question ends* |

The same situation except that it is not a young man flagging you down. The person flagging you down is an attractive young woman. There is nobody else in her car. Do you now stop to offer any help?

QUESTION 76 (non-vegetarian)

You are staying with a friend in the heart of the country. You have not long arrived when your friend has to go off to do their weekly shopping in a town some miles away. They say they'll be back in time for lunch which you've – enthusiastically or otherwise – agreed to cook. Your friend's departing words were, 'It's chicken. You'll find one out the back.' Sure enough, when you look out the back, you find several. All running around clucking their little heads off. These are the only chickens you can find and obviously the ones your friend meant. Do you kill, pluck and clean a chicken?

YES   **NO**

In chasing the free-range chickens, you slip and sprain your wrist badly. You will not be able to wring the chicken's neck when you catch one. However, you find a sharp chopper and chopping board in the kitchen. This rather messy option is your only choice. Do you still kill a chicken?

In this instance, you find the chicken already dead and plucked in the kitchen. However, it hasn't been cleaned. Do you clean and gut the chicken?

NO | **YES**   *Question ends* |

YES | **NO**   *Question ends* |

In this instance, your friend has a trout farm. Their departing words were, 'It's trout. You'll find one in the tank.' Would you kill and gut the trout?

When you return from the kitchen, you find your friend's seven-year-old daughter has turned up. She is feeding the chickens and calling each by name. She introduces you to each of them. She will be staying around but is obviously used to chickens being killed to eat. Do you still go ahead and kill a chicken?

YES | **NO**   *Question ends* |

One of the chickens happens to have your name. It is the first that you have the chance to catch. Do you catch and kill this chicken?

QUESTION 77 (male)

You are in a lift going down to the Tube platforms when an attractive girl and a man of about the same age enter the lift together. The girl comes up beside you and starts to talk to you in a very friendly manner. The man beside her looks surly and aggressive. As you reply to her, the man says, 'Look, mate, stop chatting up my girlfriend!' The girl stops talking to you. Do you try to re-engage her in conversation?

 YES   **NO**

By now the lift has descended, and you are walking along the tunnel to the platform. You are talking to the girl. The man is walking beside her on the other side. He is getting angrier and angrier. Finally, he says, 'Look, I've warned you. Stop chatting up my girlfriend.' He is about the same size as you. Do you still continue to talk to the girl?

The lift descends. The girl and the man wait together while you leave first. As you walk along the tunnel to the platform, the girl trots up beside you and starts to talk to you again. The man is a few steps behind. Before you can say anything, he repeats his warning about chatting up his girlfriend. Do you try to engage her in conversation?

 YES | **NO**   *Question ends* | **NO** | **YES**   *Question ends* |

The man storms off ahead to the platform. The girl suddenly runs off after him. When you get to the platform, they are further down it in heated but not loud argument. Finally, the man sulks off down the platform. The girl remains where she is looking away from him. She sees you and smiles sheepishly. The man is the same distance away on the other side and watching. Do you go over and continue your conversation with her?

They let you go on ahead to the platform. There are several other people already waiting. When the girl and the man arrive, the girl passes you and walks off down the platform without a glance. However, as the man passes, he points a finger at you and says in a voice loud enough for all to hear, 'Look, if I catch you bothering that girl again, I'll have you!' He then stalks off down the platform towards the girl. The eyes of all the other people there are on you. Down the platform, you can see the girl is trying to walk back towards you. The man is physically preventing her from doing so by standing in her way. However, she is now beginning to look upset. Everybody else is looking at you. Do you go and try to talk to her?

QUESTION 78   (non-vegetarian)

You are entertaining several people at your house and have laid on a large casserole and some baked potatoes. The casserole is beef, with a little bacon. This is all you have to eat in the house. Some of the people coming you don't know at all. One of them, brought by a friend, looks distinctly Arab. They could be a practising Muslim although they are dressed in Western clothes. They are the same sex as you. Knowing that a practising Muslim does not eat pork, do you warn, directly or through the friend, that there is bacon in the casserole?

 YES **NO**

When you greet the guests and offer a drink, this person immediately has a glass of whisky. Do you still warn about the bacon in the casserole?

 YES | NO   *Question ends* |

Before you can, you are waylaid by some new arrivals. While you are busy introducing people and providing drinks, you notice that this person has had a few more whiskies and is also paying rather blatant and unwelcome attentions to a close friend of yours of the opposite sex. Do you still warn the guest about the bacon in the casserole?

When you greet the guests and offer drinks, this person politely declines an alcoholic drink and has an orange juice. Do you now warn them about the bacon in the casserole?

NO | YES   *Question ends* |

As the guests prepare to eat, the Arab-looking person sniffs the casserole. They then come over and quietly ask you if there is any pork in it. Do you now tell them about the bacon in the casserole?

QUESTION 79 (female)

You are unattached and have always been attracted to a director of your company but, as far as you know, he is happily married. At an office party he tells you how he has been terribly attracted to you since you joined the company two years ago. He also tells you that he thinks he might be able to find you a more satisfying job within your department. He then asks if you would accompany him on a romantic weekend on his yacht next month. Do you accept?

 YES

The following week he asks you to take his twelve-year-old daughter for lunch as his wife has had to leave her at his office unexpectedly and he is tied up in a meeting. When you are at lunch his daughter tells you how miserable she is because her mother seems sad and her father is away from home too often. Do you still plan to accompany him on a romantic weekend for two?

 YES | NO   *Question ends* |

When you return to the office you overhear his wife confiding to someone that she is worried about her husband as he seems very depressed and uncommunicative recently. She thinks that it may be due to pressure at work and is hoping to plan a surprise holiday to help him relax and enjoy life again. Do you still proceed with your plans to accompany him on the romantic weekend for two?

 NO

The following week you receive a small bunch of exquisite white roses and a charming letter telling you that he is hopelessly in love with you and that it isn't just an office flirtation. He says that he and his wife have been unhappy for years and that he hopes to find renewed happiness in your company. You are unattached at the moment. Do you accept?

NO   · · | YES   *Question ends* |

He realizes your refusal is serious and kindly lets the matter drop. A year later, on exactly the same day, you receive another bunch of flowers and a card saying that his feelings haven't changed and that the invitation is still open. You know he has not yet split with his wife but you are still unattached. Do you accept?

QUESTION 80

A friend of yours, a nurse, rather improperly and unethically, tells you that one of the waiters at a small restaurant-cum-café that you frequent at lunchtimes has AIDS. There are only two waiters who work at the café. Do you still continue to eat there?

YES

NO

Some time later, the nurse, again rather unethically, tells you that someone else who also frequents the restaurant has since contracted AIDS. How they did so has not yet been established. There is nothing to suggest that their visits to the restaurant had anything to do with it. Do you still continue to eat there?

YES

NO   *Question ends*

The next time you are in there, you order your favourite lunch of steak and chips. There are still only two waiters. The one who brings your meal has a small blood-stained plaster on their thumb. Do you eat this meal?

You are with some friends who suggest going to this restaurant for lunch. You argue against it, even saying why you do not want to eat there. Your friends are unmoved and are all going regardless. They say that there is no chance of catching anything and obviously think that you're a bit of a worry-wart. Do you relent and go and have a meal with them?

NO

YES   *Question ends*

A few days later you bump into the proprietor of the restaurant. He remarks that he hasn't seen you there for a while and asks if you've gone off his cooking? Do you make some excuse rather than tell him the real reason?

QUESTION 81

You are staying with some friends. One evening, they have gone to the cinema. You've already seen the film so you volunteered to stay in and baby-sit. The youngest have all gone to bed. You are lounging in front of the television when their eldest child comes in – an eighteen-year-old, the same sex as you. They make themselves some coffee and join you in the lounge. While you are talking, a programme begins on television about the gay community in London. This prompts the eighteen-year-old to ask you if you have ever met anybody the same sex as you to whom you were physically attracted. Do you answer the question truthfully?

YES

NO

You are about to answer when you notice their jacket lying across the back of a chair. You can see a 'Gaylib' badge. You then realize that your friends' eldest is gay. They are quite open about it and your friends obviously must know. Do you still answer the question truthfully?

This causes a brief discussion, in which they move on to sex in general. They ask you what age you were when you first made love with somebody. Do you answer this question truthfully?

YES | NO   *Question ends*

They then ask you if you find gays offensive or distasteful. Do you answer this question truthfully?

NO | YES   *Question ends*

The discussion moves on. They then ask you if you've ever had an affair with a married person. Do you answer this question truthfully?

QUESTION 82

You are staying with a friend in the country who is organizing the local church fête. It was to have been opened by a television personality who is known as an amiable joker. The personality happens to be one of your favourites. At the last minute, the personality phones your friend. Something has cropped up and they cannot make it. The personality apologizes profusely and tells your friend that they are still free to use their name if it will help. The personality then suggests that someone could even pose as a near relative of theirs. They can even provide a prepared speech over the phone now. No one in the village knows you from a hole in the ground, so your friend asks you if you'd be prepared to do this. Do you agree?

YES

NO

While you are making notes of the speech, it becomes apparent in conversation with the personality that they do not in fact live very far from the village. There could well be people at the fête who may know the personality and their family. Do you still agree to the charade?

It becomes clear that the celebrity comes from a great distance away and there will certainly be nobody at the village fête who knows any of the celebrity's family anyway, or for that matter anything pertinent about the celebrity. Your friend has nobody else to turn to who could pose as a relative of the personality. Do you now agree to the charade?

YES | **NO** *Question ends*

Your eyes wander to a copy of the programme for the fête. You see mention of a stall run by the fan club of this celebrity. There will obviously be people there who will ask you questions that as a member of the family you should be able to answer, but you know that you don't know enough about the celebrity to be able to do so. Also, you may well be pestered by members of the fan club. Do you still agree to the charade?

NO | **YES** *Question ends*

Your friend is disappointed and unhappy. A minute or so later, the doorbell rings. It is the television personality. Apparently, they phoned from the pub around the corner as a joke. Your friend is 'highly' amused, but soon finds the whole thing genuinely funny. Over a quick drink, you find the celebrity very amusing. They suggest that you join them at the opening anyway, posing as a relative, just for a laugh. You won't be called on to say or do anything. Do you now agree?

QUESTION 83

You are stranded on a tropical island with everybody in this room and nobody else. You were all wearing flimsy summer clothing when you were stranded and have nothing else to wear. After a matter of days comes the crucial question of whether you should abandon your disintegrating clothes and institute a nudist regime or spend valuable time trying to make body covering out of natural things at hand rather than building shelters and finding food. It would be totally comfortable wearing nothing. You decide to take a vote on it. Do you vote to go nudist?

YES   **NO**

It turns out that you are outvoted. There were others who voted to go nudist though, but the vote was not binding. It was decided that those who wanted to go nudist might still do so if they wished. Do you now go nudist?

You turn out to be in a minority. Those that voted to go nudist do so. After a few days you are the only non-nudist. Now do you go nudist?

NO | **YES**   *Question ends* |

YES | **NO**   *Question ends* |

Some days later, one of the others comes back with the news that you are not alone on the island. There is a group of shipwrecked Italian sailors camped elsewhere. They do not yet know of your presence on the island. Do you still remain nudist?

In this instance, the only people marooned on the island were those in this room of the same sex as you. Would you now go nudist?

QUESTION 84

You are away from home staying in a small hotel. You have never visited this town before. You have had a pleasant meal at a small restaurant and now feel thirsty. You are strolling along the street during the warm evening looking for a pub in which to have a drink. You pop into the first likely-looking one you come across. Once through the door, you realize that this is an exclusively ethnic pub. Everybody is the same colour as you, but they are all speaking a foreign language, there is foreign music playing and you can see that the bar caters to their tastes. One or two people glance at you but more in curiosity than hostility. You are, after all, a stranger here. Do you stay in the pub and have a drink rather than wander on to find another pub?

 YES

In this instance, everybody in the pub is a different colour from you. You stick out like a sore thumb. A few people look at you, but not in any hostile way. Do you stay in this pub and have a drink rather than wandering on to find another pub?

 YES | NO   *Question ends* |

In this instance, the pub is of mixed ages and colours. It seems quite lively. Everybody is the same sex as you and you realize that this is obviously a gay pub. Do you stay here and have a drink rather than wandering on to find another pub?

 NO

You stroll on down the street and soon find another pub. When you peek into this one, you find that it is really loud and lively. Everybody is very young and wearing all sorts of strange styles of clothing, none of which is your preferred style. There is a back room where you can hear what seems to be a live band. You don't mind the music being played but you're not crazy about it either. The bar is not particularly crowded. Do you stay here for a drink rather than moving on?

 NO | YES   *Question ends* |

The next pub you come to seems very quiet. When you go in, you find out why. There is only one person in there other than the staff. An old man is sitting at the bar talking to the barman. The place is comfortable and respectable. Neither of the two even glance at you. Do you stay here for a drink rather than moving on?

QUESTION 85   (male)

You are single and at a party. There is only one woman there whom you find attractive . . . and you find her extremely attractive. In talking to her, you find that she is happily married although her husband is away for the weekend. As the evening progresses, she obviously finds you very attractive, much to her own consternation and bewilderment. She actually drops a veiled hint that although she has never been unfaithful to her husband, she might make an exception tonight – and just the one time. You do not know her husband, nor do you have any mutual friends. Do you follow up the issue?

YES

NO

You have a very enjoyable night together. However, although having said that she was willing just for a one-off one-night stand, she now says that she would love to see you again. You still find her very attractive. Do you agree to see her again?

As the evening progresses, the woman openly tells you that she finds you extremely attractive physically and emotionally and would love to spend the night with you. Just the once. Do you now accept?

NO | **YES**   *Question ends*

She now confides that she lied about being happily married. She is actually about to sue for divorce and that her husband has actually gone off for the weekend with his mistress. You still find her extremely attractive. Do you now accept?

YES | **NO**   *Question ends*

You see her again the next night and have another enjoyable time. However, you know that there is no future in the relationship. She is obviously very much in love with her husband and confused by her physical attraction to you. Also, from your characters, you know that you would never actually get on living together. However, a few days later you develop some symptoms which the doctor diagnoses as a form of VD. You have only slept with the woman in the time and you know that you must have caught it from her. Equally, if what she has told you is true, she can only have caught it from her husband who has obviously not told her. Knowing that it will cause problems with her marriage, do you tell her?

QUESTION 86

You are at a large event, such as Wimbledon. While wandering around looking for a café, you become slightly lost. You turn a corner in a quiet spot off the beaten track when you overhear a conversation from an open window. You recognize the voice, and a glance in at the window confirms that it is that of a famous politician. The politician is talking to one other person who is in the room with them. They are not aware of your presence outside. The politician belongs to a party that you do not support. You hear them saying something that if leaked to the press would be extremely embarrassing and damaging to their party. They are obviously speaking off-record. What they have said is in no way extreme, but is an obviously-well-informed comment on a current delicate political situation. Do you leak the story to the press?

 YES　　　　　　　　　　　　 **NO**

In this instance, the politician is of the party you support. However, what they are saying is really extreme and something that you disagree with totally, as would most other supporters of your party. To leak it would damage this politician but not the party. Do you still leak the story to the press?

In this instance, the politician has said something extreme which you find totally abhorrent. Up until now, you had thought this politician to be moderate and quite likeable for a member of another party. To leak the story would not damage the politician's party but could severely hamper their career. Do you now leak the story to the press?

 YES　　　| **NO**　*Question ends* |

In this instance, the politician has still said something extreme that you disagree with totally. However, to leak it would, this time, do more damage to the party you support than to the politician. Do you still leak the story to the press?

 NO　　　| **YES**　*Question ends* |

The same situation but the leaking of the story would cause acute problems for both the politician and the party to which they belong. Do you now leak the story to the press?

QUESTION 87

You are driving alone along a main road on a clear day. On the outskirts of a town you have just passed through, you see a lone male hitch-hiker. He is quite tidy-looking and in his early twenties. What's more he's holding a sign on which he's written his destination. It's about 100 miles away and happens to be where you're going. Do you stop and pick him up?

 YES

 NO

As you slow down to stop, another person, a girl, appears from behind a nearby bush. They obviously expect to be given a lift together. Do you still stop to give them a lift?

 YES | NO   *Question ends*

You are just stopping. You glance in the rear-view mirror as they start towards you. Then, another person comes from behind the bush, a second male. He's also quite tidy-looking and in his early twenties, and seems to be with the other two. Do you now give all three a lift?

As you draw nearer, you see a small American flag on the bag at his feet. He would seem to be a tourist. Do you now stop to give him a lift?

NO | YES   *Question ends*

As you draw abreast of him, you can see that his left arm, which had been concealed by his body, is in a sling. From his face, you can tell that he is actually in some pain. Do you now stop to give him a lift?

QUESTION 88

You have a small old mattress that you want to get rid of. It is too big for your dustmen to take away and the council charge to collect such rubbish. The mattress will just fit into your car without too much trouble, but you've no idea where the local authority tip is. It is probably miles away. However, there is a nearby piece of wasteland which is strewn with bits of rubbish already. Do you dump the mattress on the piece of wasteland?

 YES   **NO**

Before you have done so, you receive a pamphlet of local news. It happens to mention the wasteland and residents' concern about the rubbish there. It details the location of the local authority tip and asks that people dump their rubbish there. You glance at the details and find that the tip is a long way away, about thirty minutes' drive, and that the route is rather long and tortuous. Do you still dump the mattress on the wasteland?

 YES |NO   *Question ends*|

As you reach the wasteland, you see that it has been partly cleared. There are still one or two local residents working on the site. Hand-painted signs tell of a local residents' scheme to clear the land and build a children's playground. Do you still dump the mattress there?

The next day, you see a local authority truck clearing the wasteland. It is obviously cleared from time to time in a haphazard way. Do you now dump the mattress there?

 NO |**YES**   *Question ends*|

When you check up on the location of the local authority tip, you find that it is miles away and only open to the public for four hours each week during your working hours. What's more, the mattress seems to be acquiring several insect occupants. Do you now dump the mattress on the wasteland?

QUESTION 89

You live in a fairly isolated spot with only one other house nearby. A new family moves in. You soon realize that the father is a rough type who beats his two dogs with appalling regularity. You surmise this from their howling. Sometimes you even hear them howling all day long but you never see them. They appear to be kept locked in a shed for most of the day. Since there is no one else in the area, the family would know that any call to the RSPCA would most likely have been made by you. Do you ring the RSPCA?

YES

An RSPCA inspector calls on the family. The end result is that the man is fined and the dogs taken into care. A few days later, you find that someone has destroyed some of your favourite shrubs at the foot of the garden. Nothing happens after this. However, shortly afterwards the man has obviously acquired some more dogs from somewhere as you begin to hear howling again. Do you contact the RSPCA a second time?

YES | NO   *Question ends* |

The same as before, except that this time nothing happens to your shrubs. Instead, the man actually comes to your home and threatens you before replacing the dogs. Do you still contact the RSPCA again?

NO

One day, you actually see the dogs chained to a post in the man's garden. They are a pathetic sight and look very neglected and badly mistreated. Do you now contact the RSPCA?

NO | YES   *Question ends* |

You don't see the dogs again, though you still hear their howling. However, someone else must have learned of the plight of the dogs because you read in the local paper a sickening report of the condition the dogs were in when the RSPCA eventually intervened. The dogs were so far gone that they had to be put down. Shortly afterwards, you note that your neighbour has acquired two more. Do you now contact the RSPCA?

QUESTION 90

You have a neighbour to whom you are not particularly close but occasionally have the odd casual conversation. During one such conversation in the street, he is moaning about the state of his old car. It has failed its MOT test due to having faulty brakes. He can't afford to have them fixed at the moment and is thinking of running it without tax or insurance for a few weeks until he's raised the cash. Do you try to dissuade him?

YES

NO

A few days later, you see that he is using the car quite frequently and, in your view, unnecessarily. He seems to be avoiding you. Do you go to him and again try to dissuade him?

YES

| NO   *Question ends* |

He tells you to mind your own business and continues to drive the car. He totally ignores anything you say. Do you notify the police?

One evening, you see your neighbour narrowly avoid an accident – more by luck than design. It is clear that the car is dangerous, yet he still continues to use it. Do you now try to dissuade him or notify the authorities rather than ignore the issue?

NO

| YES   *Question ends* |

One morning, you find that his car is parked behind yours. Yours has been slightly dented. The dent is fresh and it would appear that your neighbour did it while parking. However, he denies all knowledge. Do you subsequently try to dissuade him or notify the authorities rather than do nothing about his illegal driving?

QUESTION 91

You have recently begun child minding for a neighbour to earn some extra money which you need. She is very health conscious and is extremely particular about what her toddlers eat. You have always managed to adhere to her instructions. However, today you are tired and the children are difficult. At lunchtime you discover that you are completely out of pure fruit juice and they won't accept water. You have some rather synthetic orange squash. You think this would quieten them. Do you give them the squash?

 YES   **NO**

About half an hour after giving them squash, one of your neighbour's children starts to cry and says he has a headache. When his mother returns she is concerned. She tells you that she has been worried about the frequency of these headaches but that she thought they had improved since she avoided giving him processed food. Do you show concern but not tell her about the squash?

 YES | NO   *Question ends* |

She then asks you whether there could have been any preservatives, colourings or additives in any of the food that you have given him. This information would obviously help to pinpoint the problem. You are worried about losing her trust and your useful supplementary income. Do you still avoid telling her the truth?

You decide to take the children up to the shop to buy some pure juice. When you try to get them ready to go out they play up even more. One of your neighbour's children complains that he is thirsty. You offer water again but this makes him even more cross. Do you give them some squash?

 NO | **YES**   *Question ends* |

A friend phones whom you have always regarded as a super-confident and relaxed mum. She hears crying in the background and you tell her of your dilemma. She tells you that the occasional bit of 'junk food' doesn't matter. You feel even more desperate as the volume of protest rises. With the support of another mum, do you now give them squash?

QUESTION 92

You are enjoying a holiday in Europe. You would like to stay longer – the only thing preventing you is a shortage of cash in hand. However, you discover that you can easily earn ready cash by selling some of your blood. This proves to be your only way of raising money. Do you sell your blood?

 YES

 NO

YES column:

On making enquiries, you find that there are two local clinics who will pay you for your blood. Both need it urgently but one is prepared to pay ten times what the other is offering. Do you accept the higher offer without further ado?

 YES | NO   *Question ends* |

The same situation, except that when you make your initial enquiries, you become aware that the higher offer is from a clinic specializing in trivial cosmetic surgery for wealthy people, while the lower offer is from a local clinic for poorer families who need the blood for open-heart surgery. Do you still accept the higher offer?

NO column:

Once again, you're on holiday in Europe but this time you need the money just to continue your holiday for the planned length of time as you have had your wallet and all your papers stolen. If you cannot raise any cash, you will have to cut your holiday short. Selling your blood is your only option if you wish to raise the cash. Do you now sell your blood?

 NO | YES   *Question ends* |

As before, you are on holiday in Europe but this time you are not short of cash. However, there is a tragic rail crash nearby. The local hospitals appeal for as much blood as possible. It is desperately needed to save lives. You are in a large town. Do you now give your blood?

QUESTION 93

It is a very hot spell in the middle of the summer. You have gone down to your local sports club for a cooling evening swim after work. You are one of the last people there. The person who runs the club is a close friend of yours. You are in the shower when they suddenly call out to you. They tell you that they must dash off and that you are the last person there. They simply ask you to switch off the light and shut the doors behind you when you go. You have done this several times before and it is no problem. However, when you come out of the shower, you find that someone has broken into your locker. All your clothes and belongings have been stolen, including all credit cards, cheque books, cash and any other means of instant finance. You have no money or means of payment at home so a cab is out of the question. All you have is your very large towel which will easily wrap around you. You live only a fifteen-minute walk away but through busy streets. There is no wind. Your only other option is to try phoning a friend to come and pick you up. Rather than inconvenience a friend on such a lovely evening, do you stroll home clad only in a large towel?

 YES   **NO**

In this instance, the towel is not so big. It just about covers your assets and only just wraps around you. Even then it is a tight squeeze and the side where the ends meet flaps open a bit as you walk. It is just about decent. Do you still walk home?

 YES · | **NO** *Question ends* |

You open the door to the street to find that quite a strong and gusty wind has sprung up while you were in the club. Do you still walk home?

The phone is in the foyer which has a glass wall that fronts on the street. You phone round your friends. Everybody seems to be out enjoying the fine weather. Eventually, you contact one who can come and pick you up but in an hour and a half at the earliest. Several passers-by have already stopped to look at you in amusement. You suddenly notice that the door from the foyer has swung shut and was left on self-locking by the club proprietor when they left. You will have to wait the hour and a half in the glass-fronted foyer under the gaze of the passing public. There is no shelter. Do you now choose to walk home?

 NO | **YES** *Question ends* |

With horror, a thought strikes you. The alarm system has a time setting. It is due to switch on in a few minutes after which you will not be able to leave the club. You must do so now. There are a few steps on the street outside and a canopy. You could wait there. However, do you now walk home?

QUESTION 94

You are walking along a quiet street in the late evening. There is nobody else in sight. You notice an old carrier bag in the shadows that seems unusually full. You look inside. It appears to be full of old crumpled banknotes. From the size of the bag, you'd guess about £10,000-worth. You are short of cash at the moment. Do you hand the bag and its entire contents in to the police?

 YES

 NO

On the way to the police station, the bag splits. You can see that underneath some money on top, the rest of the bag is filled with old clothes, probably the belongings of a tramp who is peacefully drunk somewhere. On rechecking, you can see that the bag only contains about £150, some old newspapers and the clothes. Do you still hand it in to the police?

Two days later, you read in the local paper that an elderly lady was brutally beaten up in her home and her life savings stolen. She had kept it in an old carrier bag. You have already spent £200 of the money settling an outstanding bill and you cannot immediately replace it. Do you now hand the bag and the remaining contents in to the police?

 YES | **NO** *Question ends*

 NO | **YES** *Question ends*

There is an emergency of some kind. The police station is a hive of activity. The policeman on duty has no time to do more than ask you to return tomorrow if it's not urgent, otherwise you may have to wait hours, even most of the night. You do not have a chance to tell him what it was about or to leave your name. You get home to find that some vandals have broken in and caused about £150-worth of damage. You are not insured. Do you still go back at some point to hand in the money to the police?

You read in the following day's paper that the old lady has died in hospital. The police have released a photofit picture of someone seen with a carrier bag fitting the description of the stolen one. The photofit was built from a description given by a courting couple who were in a car in the street where you found the bag. The photofit looks just like you. Do you now hand the bag and its contents in to the police?

QUESTION 95

You receive a chain-letter from one of the other people with whom you are playing this game. There is no list of names in the letter, simply a photocopy of the original along with instructions for you to photocopy the letter and send it to five other friends. The letter is actually very funny. It tells the story of some joker who had the brainwave of trying to send ripples of laughter around the world via the chain-letter of which you now hold a copy. It contains no threats and is not linked to any organization or cult. You find it very funny and witty. It simply asks you to spread a little humour and goodwill. Do you continue this chain letter?

 YES

 NO

In this instance, the chain letter is one that threatens bad luck to whoever breaks the chain by not sending on copies. The letter contains stories of misfortunes that befell those who did break the chain and stories of good luck about those who continued it. Do you continue the chain-letter?

In this instance, the letter is one that simply promises good luck. There are no threats about breaking the chain, and it is as amusing as in the first instance. There are some outrageously funny stories of good fortune that have befallen those who continue the chain. Do you continue this chain?

 YES | NO *Question ends*

 NO | YES *Question ends*

In this chain-letter, there is a list of twelve names. You are asked to add your name to the bottom, send £1 to the name at the top and five copies to friends. It promises that you will make a lot of money by continuing the chain. Do you continue the chain *and* send £1 to the name at the top of the list?

In this instance, there is a list of names twelve long. You are asked to add your name to the bottom of the list and to send a picture postcard from your locale to the name at the top of the list. The letter explains that this is for fun only. If you send five copies on to trustworthy friends, in due course you will receive hundreds of picture postcards from all over the world. If you have any special interests, you can even mention these beside your name so that people can send you appropriate picture postcards. Do you continue this chain?

QUESTION 96

In a crowded street market one Saturday morning, you are offered a child's BMX bicycle at a ridiculously low price. It appears to be almost new and would be a real bargain. As it happens, you know of a child who would really love to have it and whose parents, friends of yours, cannot afford to buy one. They, and you, could easily afford this one. Do you buy the bike?

 YES

 NO

YES

You suddenly remember that—as you came down the market you passed two policemen. They seemed to be on the look-out for something in particular. You would have to go back that way to get to where you parked your car. Do you still buy the bike?

YES | NO   *Question ends*

As you get your money out, you glance over the bike. You notice a clean spot on the frame, just about the size of a police registration sticker. This is a sticker that states that the bike has been registered with a certain police station. Such items have an identification number concealed somewhere on them. Do you still buy the bike?

NO

Your car is quite near the seller and it would only take an instant to buy the bike and be off. This market is also some distance from your home. Would you now buy the bike?

 NO | YES   *Question ends*

In this instance, the child you have in mind is a nephew who had such a bike but it was stolen. Would you now buy the bike?

QUESTION 97

You and your partner are away from home and sleeping in a strange bed. You both went to bed dog-tired and in need of a good night's sleep. However, you awake at three in the morning. It is pitch dark. After tossing and turning a bit, you realize that you will be unable to get back to sleep for a while. At your bedside is a good book which you could read, and, in fact, are interested in reading. However, you can't find the book without putting the light on, let alone read it. Your partner is sleeping lightly and could well wake up if you switch the light on. The light and switch are on your side of the bed. Do you switch the light on?

 YES

 NO

Before you went to bed the previous night, your partner complained of feeling ill and seemed to have a slight temperature. They seem to be having a fairly restless night, though they have not actually woken up at all. Would you still switch on the light?

After another hour, you are still awake and far from sleepy. You feel the light. It is heavily shaded and can be angled away from your partner. Do you now switch on the light?

 YES   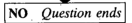| **NO** *Question ends* |

NO

| **YES** *Question ends* |

In this instance, your partner has had trouble sleeping recently. This appears to be the first good night's sleep they are getting for some time. Would you still switch on the light?

Shortly, your partner begins to snore deeply. They are obviously very soundly asleep. On the other hand, their snoring will definitely prevent you from falling asleep. Do you now switch on the light?

QUESTION 98

You have just had a very fine meal at a restaurant. As you leave, you discover that you have lost your cloakroom ticket but you can see your coat, which you point out to the attendant. When you get home, you realize that the coat is not yours. It is identical in size, style and colour but is in slightly better condition as it is newer. It is now late and the restaurant will be closed. You will have to return tomorrow. There is nothing in the pockets of this coat, nor was there anything in the pockets of yours. Do you take the coat back?

 YES   **NO**

In this instance, when you get home you also find an expensive gold pen in the pocket of the coat. It is initialled. Do you still take the coat back?

 YES | **NO**   *Question ends* |

In this instance, there is no pen. Instead you find four £50 notes folded up in a small pocket. Do you still take the coat back?

The next day, as you pick up the coat, something heavy bangs against you. You feel the hem. Something has been stitched into the lining. You find a concealed flap and discover that the object is a stiletto knife. You also find another concealed flap in the lining. This contains a small sachet containing a few ounces of white powder. Do you now take the coat and its contents back to the restaurant?

NO | **YES**   *Question ends* |

In this instance, you had left something in your own coat. It was nothing important – just an old letter. However, it mentioned your name though not your address. The sender's name and address were on it, so someone could trace you from it if they tried hard enough. Do you now take the coat back to the restaurant?

QUESTION 99

You are at work. One lunchtime a young female secretary confides to you that she is being harassed by her superior. This man, considerably older than her, insists on taking her to meetings with him and so far has merely tried to hold hands with her *en route*. The girl is too shy and embarrassed to do anything about it herself and does not want to get the man in trouble. The man is not your superior; you and he are equals. You reassure the girl, but do you now do nothing rather than take issue with, or bring pressure to bear on, the man or report him to personnel?

YES	NO

The girl comes to you again; the man has now tried to kiss her on the cheek, repeatedly. Do you still do nothing?

YES | NO   *Question ends* |

The man has now tried to fondle the girl and continually pesters her whenever they are alone together. The girl is now very upset and flustered. You are the only one she has confided in and she is too shy to do anything about it herself. Do you still do nothing?

The man shows no response to anybody talking to him or to any pressure. The only option is to report him to personnel. However, you know the man has recently been through a traumatic divorce, although he is no friend of yours. Do you now do nothing?

NO | YES   *Question ends* |

The same situation, except that the man is your superior. It is he who hired you and can fire you, or make life very difficult for you. Do you now do nothing?

QUESTION 100

Your neighbour's tree prevents light coming into your kitchen and is a definite nuisance. You both agreed long ago that it should come down, even though it is quite an attractive tree. You have arranged to help him do it on the next Saturday morning. However, the night before, you mention it to an environmentalist friend who says that she thinks that the tree might be the subject of a tree preservation order as there are quite a few related to the area. The next morning do you help your neighbour cut down the tree rather than wait to make further enquiries about any tree preservation order?

YES   **NO**

The only difference is that your environmentalist friend tells you that there is definitely a tree preservation order on the tree. She is certain of this and you know her to be reliable on matters of this nature. What's more, she tells you of a recent case in which the owner of a protected tree was fined £100 for cutting it down. Do you keep quiet and help your neighbour even though you may be making him liable for such a fine?

YES | NO   *Question ends* |

As you prepare to cut down the tree on the Saturday morning, your neighbour jokingly says that he hopes there isn't a tree preservation order on it. Do you still keep quiet?

Your neighbour tells you that he's prepared to take any risks involved in the tree having a perservation order on it. As far as he's concerned, it's now or never. Do you help him or allow him to do it rather than try to dissuade him for the time being?

NO | YES   *Question ends* |

If you had recently had a surveyor round to check your house and found that the tree's roots were causing damage to your house and that repairs would become rather expensive if nothing were done about it, would you then help your neighbour rather than wait to find out about any preservation order?

QUESTION 101

You buy a really cheap radio, for under £10, from a shop. It soon turns out to be faulty. You can still get all the stations you want on it but the sound crackles badly and is clearly not as intended by the manufacturer. Do you take the radio back to the shop and complain?

 YES

 NO

The shop is a fair trek away and not one you normally frequent, so they don't know you there. As you prepare to go, you find that you have lost the receipt. Do you still take the radio back to the shop?

In this instance, you have not bought the radio for yourself. You have picked it up on behalf of a friend. They had seen it in the window when the shop was closed. Since you live nearer the shop, they gave you the money and asked you to pick it up for them. You will be seeing them in a couple of days' time. Do you now take the radio back to the shop?

 YES — | **NO** *Question ends* |

In this instance, you did not buy the radio. It was given away free with another more expensive appliance, which you bought and is working perfectly. Do you still take the radio back?

 NO | **YES** *Question ends* |

In this instance, you have bought the radio on behalf of a child with money that they have saved up over a few months. Now do you take the radio back?

QUESTION 102

You are out of work and quite broke. An acquaintance gives you a contact and tells you that this person produces pornographic magazines and that you would be guaranteed to earn some money by posing for pornographic photos. You are desperate for some cash. Do you follow up the contact?

 YES   **NO**

You are offered ample payment to pose for some photos in which you indulge in straight sex with a member of the opposite sex. You are even told that, since it is your first session, you can pick your partner from the other models to make sure it is someone you prefer. Do you accept the offer?

The acquaintance explains that some of the work available through the contact is 'soft porn'. You would only be asked to pose naked, on your own in 'tasteful' surroundings. You are now even more hard up and have several unpaid bills for services (electricity, phone, etc). Do you now follow up the contact?

YES | NO   *Question ends* | **NO** | YES   *Question ends* |

Later, you are offered more work. You are asked to feign certain activities that you find offensive. It is made clear that you only pretend and that you can choose your partner as before. The pay is much higher and you are still short of cash. Do you accept this offer?

The acquaintance adds that there is some work posing scantily clad with none of the important bits revealed. Once again, you would be photographed on your own in 'tasteful' surroundings. You still have the same unpaid bills. Do you now follow up the contact?

YES | NO   *Question ends* |

You are now offered a great deal of money to perform the activities which you find offensive live for a film. Do you accept this offer?

QUESTION 103

You are travelling on the London Tube when it stops at a station. Just as the doors are about to close, you see someone running down the steps on to the platform. They are obviously hoping to catch the train. You are standing right by the nearest doors to them. By simply sticking your foot out you can stop the doors from closing to allow the person to get on the train. The person is perfectly ordinary, in their mid-thirties wearing smart but casual clothes and of the same sex as you. Do you stop the doors from closing?

 YES

 NO

In this instance, you are in a hurry yourself, and the train has already been waiting in the station for some while. You have a train to catch elsewhere and time is tight. Do you still stop the doors from closing?

 YES | **NO** *Question ends* |

As you move to do so, you suddenly become aware of several other footsteps rushing down the stairs behind the person you can see. It sounds as though it's a party of people. Do you still stop the doors from closing?

As you see their face more clearly, it is obvious that they are desperate to catch the train. Do you now hold the doors open?

 NO | **YES** *Question ends* |

As they swing round the corner towards the train, their shoulder bag slides round. Protruding from the side pouch, you can see the top of an airline ticket. They evidently have a plane to catch, urgently. Do you now hold the doors open?

QUESTION 104

You have just been done in the magistrates' court for some minor traffic offence. Yours was the last case of the day. Outside, as you are heading home, you see the chairman of the magistrates who tried you getting into his car. You can see that one of the tyres on the side nearest you is flat. He is on the far side of the car and oblivious to this. Do you tell him of his misfortune?

YES   **NO**

In this instance, you had a distinct impression during your hearing that the chairman had taken against you. Do you still tell him of his misfortune?

You are almost alongside the car as he gets in. There is nobody else around. As he climbs into the car, he gives you a mildly disapproving look. You realize that if you say nothing, he may well conclude that you let down or damaged his tyre. Do you now say anything?

 YES | NO   *Question ends* |

In this instance, the chairman had still given the impression that he disapproved of you and your traffic offence. However, his tyre is not flat. Instead, when he switches on his lights, you can see that his rear lights aren't working. Do you tell him about this?

 NO | YES   *Question ends* |

The same situation so far, except that your hearing has not yet been concluded and you must return tomorrow. Do you now tell him about the flat tyre?

QUESTION 105

You are at a party. You do not know the people whose house it is as they are friends of a friend of yours. You get roaring drunk. You struggle to the bathroom, which turns out to be occupied. As you search for elsewhere, time runs out and you are sick on your hosts' bedroom carpet. You don't think anyone has spotted you. Do you own up to the hosts?

YES

Far from admiring your honesty, your hosts make a great fuss about it and seem to take a perverse pleasure in telling everyone about your 'abominable' behaviour. You find their reaction unfriendly.

Some time later, you are throwing a party. Your previous hosts turn up, uninvited. Do you let them in?

YES | NO   *Question ends*

After they and you have had a few drinks, do you take the opportunity to bring up – so to speak – the incident at their party and your views on it?

NO

Shortly after you rejoin the party, you hear somebody shouting from upstairs that somebody has been sick. Looking down, you can see that your clothes bear traces of the crime. You see the host coming down the stairs looking very angry. He looks intent on finding the culprit. Do you intercept him and quietly own up to avoid any possible scene?

NO | YES   *Question ends*

Before you have had a chance to clean up, the host spots the telltale traces on your clothes. He approaches you and asks you if you've anything to say for yourself. Do you now own up rather than feign ignorance or make up some cock-and-bull story?

QUESTION 106

You are walking home through your local park. Staggering along the path towards you is a youth. He has glassy eyes. You can see part of a plastic bag sticking out from his pocket and he reeks of glue. As you pass, he seems to have a fit of some kind. He drops to the ground like a sack of potatoes, twitches and becomes still. You can see immediately that he has stopped breathing. There is nobody else around. Do you try to administer any form of resuscitation?

YES   **NO**

He does not respond to any massage. The only other option is the kiss of life. However, as you turn him, you nearly choke on the smell of booze and glue from his mouth. Do you still try to administer mouth-to-mouth resuscitation?

You are just easing off down the path when a teenage girl staggers from some nearby bushes. She runs to the fallen youth and screams. Since you are the only person around, she calls to you for help. Do you now go back and try to administer any form of resuscitation?

YES | NO *Question ends* | **NO** | YES *Question ends* |

You loosen his jacket and notice a 'Gaylib' badge. You also notice a cold sore on the young man's lip. Do you still administer mouth-to-mouth resuscitation?

Just then, you see some other people appear, attracted by the girl's scream. There are a couple and a park attendant. You realize that to all concerned, the accident has just happened behind you. Nobody knows you have left the youth to his fate. Do you now go back to join the others and try to help?

QUESTION 107

You are in your local supermarket picking up some shopping. You need some apples. However, the only ones that they have are clearly marked as South African. There are several other shops in the area. Do you buy the South African apples?

YES

You hear on the news that an anti-apartheid group has said that it will carry out a campaign in which South African produce in shops will be sprayed with human blood. The next time you go to the supermarket, you pass by the rear entrance. The door is open and you can see some staff washing and wiping apples. When you enter the supermarket, there are no apples to be seen but an assistant appears from the back with a trolley laden with apples and proceeds to put them on display. They are marked as South African. Do you buy these apples?

YES | NO   Question ends |

The anti-apartheid group announces another campaign. South African produce will be injected with a mild poison that may produce stomach pains but nothing more serious. The only apples in the shops in your area are South African. You wish to buy some apples. Do you buy the South African ones?

NO

You are out shopping. You wish to buy some apples. However, the cheapest apples are South African while all the others look rather tasteless and are twice the price at least. Do you buy the South African apples?

NO | YES   Question ends |

You are having a dinner party. You are in a hurry and need some apples, which are essential to your planned meal. The only ones you can find are South African. Do you buy them?

QUESTION 108

You are on your way home late one summer's night. In your street a young foreigner stops you to ask directions. In conversation, you find that they have just arrived in this country to find work. They have found a job in a restaurant and had been staying in a bed and breakfast place but their money ran out before they received their first pay packet. They are now looking for somewhere else to stay. The person is the same sex and colour as you and seems respectable and pleasant. However, their English is not fluent though they speak enough to get by. You do not speak their language. The weather is warm and dry. You live only a few doors away and have a spare bedroom that is rarely used. Do you offer to put them up for the night?

 YES

 NO

The situation is the same, except that your flat is small and you have no spare bedroom. If you were to put them up they would have to sleep on the sofa in your only room other than your bedroom. Do you still offer to put them up for the night?

 YES | NO   *Question ends* |

The situation is the same, in that your flat is small and they would have to sleep on the sofa, but the person is of a different colour from you. Do you offer to put them up for the night?

The situation is the same, except that it is a winter's night. The weather is very cold and it looks as though it might rain. Do you offer the person a room for the night?

 NO | **YES**   *Question ends* |

It is the summer night again, but this time the person is of the opposite sex to you. You find them attractive. Do you offer them a room for the night?

QUESTION 109

You are walking home beside the river. As you pass a weir, you can see a bedraggled cat lying half in the water and half on the river-bank. It is miaowing plaintively and is obviously exhausted and in imminent danger of being swept off towards the weir. The river-bank is steep, muddy and slippery. You are wearing some old casual clothes. There is no one else around as far as you can see. Do you go down the river-bank to try to save the cat?

 YES   **NO**

The situation is exactly as before, except that you are wearing your best clothes. Do you still go down the muddy, slippery bank to try to save the cat?

 YES | NO   *Question ends* |

The situation is the same as before, except that not only are you wearing your best clothes but you are on your way to a job interview. You don't have any time to spare if you are to arrive on time and it is a job that you are keenly interested in. Do you still go down the muddy river-bank to try to save the cat?

The situation is the same as before, except that this time there is a young girl on the riverside. She calls your attention to the cat and asks you to save it. There is no one else around. Do you now attempt to save the cat?

 NO | YES   *Question ends* |

Once again, the situation is the same as before, except that you are with your partner who you know cannot swim and is afraid of falling into the river. They call your attention to the cat and ask you to save it. Do you now try to save the cat?

QUESTION 110

You have had an argument with your partner the evening before. When you parted, you were both equally angry with each other. Overnight, you have realized that you were both equally at fault. You know your partner's temperament well enough to know that they will not contact you for at least a week. Despite occasional arguments, you both think the world of each other and would want to continue seeing each other. Do you try to contact them first?

YES   NO

The same situation, except that you believe that your partner was totally in the wrong in this instance. Even if they were to agree with this, you know them well enough to know that they will still not get in touch with you for at least a week. Do you still contact them first?

The same situation, except that overnight you have come to the conclusion that you were totally in the wrong. You know your partner well enough to realize that they will not contact you for at least a week. Do you try to contact them first?

YES | NO   *Question ends* | **NO** | YES   *Question ends* |

The original situation where you think that you were both equally to blame, except that you know your partner well enough to know that they will contact you at the first opportunity. Do you still try to contact them first?

The same situation, in that you believe that you were in the wrong, except that in just over a week's time your partner is due to go on a month's holiday. You know them well enough to know that they are unlikely to contact you before this. You still think the world of each other and you know that this would not endanger the relationship. Do you try to contact them first?

QUESTION 111

You are at work. You and a fellow worker are with a valued client of the company. During the course of the conversation, your fellow worker claims credit for something you have done. You do not know this fellow worker, but they are of the same status as you within the company. Do you dispute their claim, in any way, in front of the client?

 YES

 NO

This time your superior claims credit for your work in discussion with one of your colleagues. You are present. Your colleague does not know that the work was yours. There is nobody else there. Do you dispute your superior's claim then and there?

 YES

| **NO** *Question ends* |

This time your superior claims credit for your work in front of a prospective new client. You are the only other person present. Do you, in any way, dispute your superior's claim then and there?

The client leaves. You are alone with your fellow worker. However, the situation is slightly different in that you know they are renowned for claiming credit for things that they have not done. Everybody knows this and you know that nothing you say will change them. This is the first time that they have done it to you, though. Do you now dispute their claim with them?

 NO

| **YES** *Question ends* |

The same situation, except that the fellow worker is unknown to you. You do not know whether they have done this sort of thing before. Do you now dispute their claim with them?

QUESTION 112

You are on the telephone to your partner and have been having a long argument. Your partner is very angry, as are you, and the argument is going nowhere. It has not yet degenerated into abuse but is likely to. Do you simply hang up?

YES

NO

The telephone rings and you answer it. It is your partner and they are even angrier. Do you hang up again?

Your partner becomes more and more angry. Insults, extremely hurtful ones, are showered upon you. Do you hang up now?

YES

| NO   Question ends |

The telephone immediately rings again. Do you not even bother to answer it?

NO

| YES   Question ends |

You get a telephone call. It is a salesman who begins to extol the virtues of his company's double glazing. You are not the least bit interested. However, the salesman proceeds on automatic despite your protestations that you don't even have any windows in your home. He continues regardless of what you say. Do you now hang up?

QUESTION 113

Your work takes you abroad for a short spell during which you must live in another country. One of your colleagues there breaks the local laws. You do not know this person very well and neither like nor dislike them. They are of your nationality. The authorities come to ask you some questions. The situation is such that you know this person is guilty of the crime. If you tell the authorities what you know, the person will be convicted. If, on the other hand, you plead ignorance, they cannot even be arrested. There is no possible comeback on you either way. You have taken no part in the crime nor have you benefited from it in any way. The person has been dealing illegally in uncut gems that are mined locally. The punishment is from five to ten years in one of the rather unsavoury local prisons. When the authorities ask you, do you tell them what you know?

 YES   **NO**

In this instance, their crime was stealing uncut gems. The punishment for this is to have the right hand cut off. Do you still tell the authorities what you know?

 YES | NO   *Question ends* |

In this instance, the person has been trafficking in drugs. The punishment for this is execution by hanging. Do you still tell the authorities what you know?

In this instance, the person's crime was that they were illegally-selling alcohol. The punishment for this is a public flogging. Do you now tell the authorities what you know?

 NO | YES   *Question ends* |

Once again, the crime was illegally selling alcohol, but this time the punishment is that they will simply be deported. Do you now tell the authorities what you know?

QUESTION 114

Your neighbours, with whom you are quite friendly, go on holiday. They leave you their house and car keys, and ask you just to pop in, water the plants occasionally and generally keep an eye on things for them. Their car is kept parked in the street outside their house. It is a new car and is very impressive. It is your favourite model and style. They have given you the keys so that you can move it if necessary while they are away. A few days after they have gone, you are going to a special social function. Their car is much more impressive than yours. Your insurance is for your own car only. You do not know if you would be covered by your neighbour's insurance. Do you use their car?

YES

It handles like a dream. You're very impressed with it. A few days later, you're popping into town to get some shopping. However, your car is parked about fifteen minutes' walk away as it was the nearest parking space you could find when you got home late the night before. Their car is still parked right outside. Do you use their car rather than walk to your own?

YES | NO   *Question ends*

You drive into town and do your shopping. When you return to the car, you see to your horror that someone has collided with it, evidently while parking. The grille, wing and headlights are damaged. It would cost more than you can really afford to get it repaired. You do not know if your neighbour's insurance would cover this eventuality. However, you could just leave it outside their house as though it had been there all the time and claim that somebody collided with it there. Nobody else in the street has seen you use the car. Do you do this?

NO

One morning, you're late for work. Your car is parked some fifteen minutes' walk away as this was the nearest you could get when you got home late last night. Your neighbour's car is still parked right outside. If you use that, you could just get to work on time. Do you now use your neighbour's car?

NO | YES   *Question ends*

In this instance, your neighbour's car is an old jalopy full of junk and dirt. The boot is particularly mucky. Your car, however, is your pride and joy. It is brand new. You have some rubbish to take to the local tip, which you must do immediately as it is starting to smell. There is no way you can take it in your car without some filth rubbing off on to your car. Do you use your neighbour's car for this as it won't make much different if it gets a bit dirtier?

QUESTION 115

You have been to a show in the West End of London. As you wend your way back to your car down a side alley beside a smart shop, you notice that the side display window of the shop has been smashed. There are no alarm bells ringing, no sirens to be heard and nobody else in sight. Displayed in the window by the hole is a timeless classic-style pullover in a plain colour. It has a tag by it showing the price as £60. It looks as though it is your size. You wave your hand through the hole in the glass. There is no hidden eye alarm. You can easily reach the pullover. Do you take it?

YES

You notice another pullover a bit further along the window. You do not like the style of this and it does not look to be remotely your size. However, it is labelled as cashmere and priced at £300. You can reach this by crawling just inside the window. Do you grab this as well?

YES | NO *Question ends* |

As your eyes adjust, you can see racks of very expensive cashmere sweaters at the back of the shop. Some you like the look of. However, you will have to go right into the shop. Do you go in and loot what you like while the going is good?

NO

In this instance, the sweater in the window is labelled as pure cashmere and price-tagged at £300. You like the style and colour very much and you can see on the label that it is your size. It is within easy reach. Do you reach in and take it?

NO | YES *Question ends* |

On this occasion, your partner is with you. It is they who like the £300 cashmere sweater and they whom it would fit. However, they cannot reach it as they are shorter than you. You can reach it. They ask you to get it for them. Do you now take the sweater?

QUESTION 116

Some friends unexpectedly phone to say that they are passing through your town and ask if they could drop in for a light lunch and to see you. You hurriedly make some bean soup. Only after you have popped in some meat stock do you remember that one of the group is a vegetarian. This person is a friend of your friends in the group and you have only met them on a few occasions before. Do you serve them the bean soup anyway?

 YES **NO**

The vegetarian comments on how tasty the soup is and asks you what's in it. Do you omit to mention the meat stock?

 YES | NO   *Question ends* |

The same initial situation, except that the vegetarian in the group is also your best friend in the group. They are very sincere in their views. Would you serve them the bean soup?

You decide to put the soup to one side and you make macaroni cheese instead. It is just ready as the group arrives. When you put it on the table, the vegetarian says that they are off dairy products for health reasons and are sorry that it wasn't mentioned on the phone. Do you offer them the bean soup instead, omitting to mention the meat stock?

NO | YES   *Question ends* |

The same situation, except that the vegetarian on seeing the macaroni cheese proceeds to give a 'holier-than-thou' discourse on what people should eat. All in all they prove to be a bit of a pain in the neck. Do you offer them the bean soup, omitting to mention the meat stock?

QUESTION 117

You have been travelling in Turkey and have spent a few pleasant days with a couple of jovial middle-aged Englishwomen whom you met *en route*. You all happen to be flying back to London together. At the airport, one of them tells you that she wants to take three litres of spirits back home. As you are under the duty-free limit and do not want any more of your own, she asks you if you would agree to take one of her bottles through customs for her. She has two bottles in a see-through duty free bag. She says that the third bottle is hidden among a bundle of clothes in the bottom of her small canvas shoulder bag. It is this bag that you must carry through customs. The flight is called and you are approaching customs. There is not time to examine inside the bag but you can feel a bottle in there. Do you agree to carry it through for her?

 YES   **NO**

The situation is the same except that carrying the bottle would take you half a litre over the duty free limit. Do you still agree?

 YES | **NO** *Question ends* |

You are back to the original situation where you are not over the duty-free limit. You take the bag. However, as you approach customs, she appears nervous and seems to be keeping her distance. Do you carry on and take her bag through?

She tries frantically to return one of her bottles to the duty-free shop but they won't take it back. Also, it turns out, she does not have the money to declare it and pay any duty. Do you now take her canvas shoulder bag through the customs for her?

 NO | **YES** *Question ends* |

The same situation, except that she just has enough time to show you a bottle of some rough-looking locally produced spirit concealed among her clothes and toiletry containers in the bag. Do you now agree to carry the bag through?

QUESTION 118

During a long affair, your lover tells you a highly embarrassing secret about themselves. You are the only one that they have ever told and they ask you never to tell anyone else. You split up rather acrimoniously. Some mutual friends during a conversation with you make some remarks about your ex and hint that you probably know some choice secrets. Do you tell them the secret?

 YES   **NO**

YES

Your ex hears about this and telephones you. They are very upset. They ask you please to tell nobody else and remind you that they know things about you that they have never told anyone. These secrets of yours are only mildly embarrassing and would cause you no great discomfort. Do you tell any other mutual friends your ex's secret should the circumstances arise?

 YES | NO   *Question ends* |

Your ex telephones you again. They are incredibly depressed because you have spread their secret. They are in a terrible emotional state and seem to hint that if you continue to spread their secret, it would be the end. They seem possibly suicidal. Do you still continue to tell mutual friends should the occasion arise?

NO

Some mutual friends tell you that your ex has been spreading some rather nasty but obviously untrue rumours about you. These stories do you no harm since your friends know you well enough to see through them. In passing, your mutual friends ask about your ex. Do you tell them the secret?

NO | **YES**   *Question ends* |

You now hear that your ex has been revealing some highly embarrassing secrets that they know about you. These you know to be true, and the matter has caused difficulty between you and your friends. Should any mutual friends enquire, would you now tell them your ex's secret?

QUESTION 119

You come home to find that you have been burgled. Your stereo and other similar items have been stolen. However, only some of the stolen items were insured. Do you report some other insured items as stolen when they haven't been at least to make up the value of the uninsured items?

 YES

 NO

The same situation, except that all the stolen items were insured. Do you still report some other items as stolen so as to be able to claim more on the insurance?

 YES

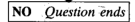 **NO** *Question ends*

The same except that you must have disturbed the house-breakers on your return. Your house has been broken into but nothing has been stolen. There are signs of the break-in, however. Do you report anything as stolen to claim money on the insurance?

The same situation, except that you share the house or flat with some others. You are the only one who has had anything stolen. However, all the others are going to report various items as stolen to make money on the insurance. Do you now report some additional items stolen at least to cover the value of the uninsured items that were taken?

 NO

YES *Question ends*

The police come. While talking to you, they list your stolen items and add that they believe various other things were stolen from the others in the house. They ask you to verify this. Do you verify the false claims of the others?

QUESTION 120 (smoker)

You are visiting someone's home. You have never been there before and it is the first time that you have met your hosts as you have gone there with some friends. You are sitting talking. Nobody else is smoking and you would like a cigarette. However, you can see no ash-trays anywhere. The host is engaged in conversation with one of your friends. Do you start smoking a cigarette rather than waiting for an opportunity to ask whether your host objects?

 YES   **NO**

Your host politely comments that he disapproves of smoking and thinks it an objectionable habit. Although it causes him no discomfort, as he used to smoke himself, he adds that he would rather that you did not smoke in his home. However, he does not expressly forbid it.

Do you continue to smoke while there?

 YES | NO · *Question ends* |

On the way home, you have just caught the last train. You had to run and leap in the nearest compartment. It is a non-smoker. It is a fast train and does not stop until it reaches your destination, a journey of an hour and a half. There is nobody else in the compartment and there are no connecting doors between the carriages. You are dying for a cigarette. Do you smoke one?

When you ask your host, he politely tells you that he does not allow smoking in his home as he finds it highly objectionable and it causes him discomfort.

At a later date, he is visiting your home with some mutual friends. They will be there practically all day. Do you smoke in your own home while he is there?

NO | YES *Question ends* |

In the original situation, you are on your way home. You have just caught the last train and are sitting in a smoking compartment. The train is non-stop to your destination and the journey takes an hour and a half. There are no connecting doors between compartments. As the train pulls out, a young man comes running up and jumps in as it is the nearest compartment to the entrance. You have been dying for a cigarette after going without one at your host's. You light one up. The young man politely asks if you'd mind not smoking as he finds it objectionable. Do you, however, smoke a cigarette on the journey?

QUESTION 121

You are at work. A colleague whom you know only through work praises enthusiastically some work for which they believe you to be responsible and your abilities at doing the work. The work was in fact done by someone who has since left the company. Nobody currently at the company knows either that person or who is responsible for the work being praised. Do you give the credit where it is due rather than remain silent and take the credit yourself?

YES

NO

The situation is the same, except that the work is being praised by your new superior who has only just joined the company. They believe the work to be yours and praise you. Do you give the credit where it is due rather than remain silent and take the credit yourself?

The situation is the same, except that the person who actually did the work is still with the company. They are no friend of yours, however, and happen to be quiet and retiring, rarely speaking up for themselves. Do you give the credit where it is due rather than remain silent and take the credit yourself?

YES

NO *Question ends*

You go for an interview for a job which you want really badly. It is just what you've always been looking for. However, during the interview, your interviewer looks at some of your previous work and begins to praise an item. You were not responsible for the aspect of the work which they are praising. They refer to the part that you actually did as average and obviously believe you to be responsible for the praiseworthy part. Do you now give credit where it is due rather than remain silent and take the credit yourself?

NO

YES *Question ends*

The same situation, except that the person who did the work is a close friend of yours and is still working for the company. However, they are quiet and retiring and rarely speak up for themselves. Do you give the credit where it is due rather than remain silent and take the credit yourself?

QUESTION 122

A foreign tourist stops you in the street. They cannot speak a word of English and start asking you apparently complicated questions by means of much gesticulation and words in a language you cannot even identify, let alone speak or understand. It will clearly take a great deal of time and effort to deal with their enquiry, whatever it may turn out to be. You are not in any particular hurry, though. Do you try to help them?

YES

This time there are two tourists. As you are gesticulating with them, they spend a lot of time commenting to each other in their own language and laughing, possibly at you – you have no idea. Do you still continue to try to help them?

YES | **NO** *Question ends*

Without asking, one of them starts to photograph you and their friend struggling to communicate. They then begin to get physical, slapping you on the back cheerfully and crowding you. Do you still continue to try and help them?

NO

Before you go on your way, the tourist signals that they would like to buy you a drink at the pub you are standing outside so that you can enjoy a drink in the sunshine while you help them. Do you now try to help them?

NO | **YES** *Question ends*

If the tourist were of the opposite sex to you and very attractive, would you then try to help them?

QUESTION 123

On a crowded morning, you are waiting for a driver to pull out of a parking space so that you can park. It seems to be the only space available. The driver leaves but before you can manoeuvre, another smaller car nips in. The driver is a middle-aged businessman who is obviously pretending not to have noticed you. Do you remonstrate with him?

 YES

 NO

The same situation, except that the driver of the other car is a myopic old lady who clearly had not seen you and had not meant to 'jump the queue'. Would you still remonstrate?

The same situation except that the driver of the other car is a young lad who laughs and merrily gives you a V sign. Would you remonstrate with him?

 YES | **NO**   *Question ends* |

 NO | **YES**   *Question ends* |

As you wind down your window to do so, a large fellow runs up to her car. He is about six feet tall and greets her in a loud self-confident manner. Do you still remonstrate with her?

The driver is still the young lad, but this time you have a friend in your car. Your friend is a large eager chap who is all for giving the cheeky young lad a bit of his mind. Do you encourage him to do so?

QUESTION 124

You are in a restaurant. The food has been very good, though not outstanding, and the service has been very efficient and friendly. When you get the bill, service has been included. You are not short of cash. Do you also leave a tip for the waiter?

 YES   **NO**

You are in another restaurant; this time the food has not been particularly good, but the service has been very efficient though not particularly friendly. Once again, service has been included in the bill and you are not short of cash. Do you still leave a tip for the waiter?

 YES | **NO**   *Question ends* |

You are in a small snack bar having a quick bite to eat. Simply some coffee and a few cakes or sandwiches. The food is much as you would expect in such a place and the service is a bit haphazard, though really not bad. Once again, service is included in the bill and you are not short of cash. Do you leave a tip for the waiter?

You are in a small friendly restaurant. However, the food is not particularly good. The waiter is extremely overworked and consequently the service is slow. However, he is obviously doing his best to cater as best he can amid the chaos, apologizing for any long delays and being friendly, amusing and as helpful as possible in the circumstances. Once again, service is included in the bill and you are not short of cash. Do you leave the waiter a tip?

NO | **YES**   *Question ends* |

You are on holiday. Having overspent wildly the night before, you seek out a small, cheap back-street restaurant. By the time you find one, all others are either full or closed. It is your only option. It is rather bizarre. The walls are decorated with local items among which are hanging some battered chest-expanders and pictures of body-builders. The pugnacious *patron* is entrenched in a corner downing beer with some cronies; his wife is left to serve and cook. You will never forget her. Her eyes are sunken and darkly bagged. She is pale and nervous, occasionally casting frightened glances in her husband's direction, and during the course of the meal, you notice deep bruises on her neck and arms as her blouse shifts. She hastily covers them on each occasion. The food is appalling. The meat even tastes rancid. However, the woman is polite and does her very best to please. Once again, the bill includes service, and you have the spare cash. Do you leave her a tip?

QUESTION 125

You are walking in the street when a tramp approaches you. He is not exactly clad in rags, nor is he drunk or obnoxious. However, he looks far from respectable. He asks for 50p for a cup of coffee. You are not broke. Do you give him the 50p?

 YES

 NO

The same situation, except that the tramp is slightly drunk. He is not rude, though. You suspect that coffee is the last thing that he will spend the money on. Do you give him the 50p?

The same situation, except that the tramp seems a genuine 'man of the road'. He is actually semi-respectably dressed although a little frayed around the edges, and is quite amusing in the way he speaks to you. Do you give him the 50p he is asking for?

 YES | **NO**   *Question ends* |

This time you are approached by a woman who looks pretty rough and ready. Probably a gypsy. She has a small dirty child with her and gives you a smooth line about her husband being sick and needing money to feed her child. She is obviously a professional beggar. Do you give her the 50p she is asking for?

 NO | **YES**   *Question ends* |

You are approached by a respectable-looking young man. He explains that he is a student hitch-hiking through and has been dropped in the centre of town. He needs 50p to catch a bus out of town, a five-mile walk, to where he can hitch a lift. Do you give him the 50p he is asking for?

QUESTION 126

You are at a formal party. Standing by himself is a respectably dressed young man – but his flies are undone. You alone seem to have noticed this. You have never spoken to or seen him before. Do you tell him that his flies are undone?

 YES   **NO**

As you approach him, you can tell by a slight unsteadiness in his stance and a glazed look in his eye, not to mention his breath, that he is very drunk. Do you still tell him that his flies are undone?

He is looking a little lost and nervous. He seems to be steeling himself to enter the main rooms where most of the guests are. Do you now tell him that his flies are undone?

 YES | NO   *Question ends* | **NO** | YES   *Question ends* |

From the look he gives you as you approach and the way he looks at some of the other guests, you realize that it could be, although you're not sure, that he is perfectly aware that his flies are undone. Do you still tell him?

Just then, you see a group who spot him from a distance and begin to make their way towards him. In the group is the guest of honour – an eminently shockable lady in her sixties. The group are obviously about to introduce the young man to her. There is just time. Do you tell the young man that his flies are undone?

QUESTION 127

You notice that your neighbour's dog has come through your boundary and defecated liberally in the middle of your lawn. You have always had a civil but strained relationship with your neighbour and this has happened before. You have spoken to him on the subject but it has made little difference. Do you scoop up the offending faeces and, surreptitiously, dump them over the boundary into the neighbour's garden?

 YES   **NO**

As you are about to do so, your neighbour comes out into his garden. However, he has not seen you standing by the boundary. Do you still dump them into his garden this time?

 YES | NO   *Question ends* |

Before you can do so, he turns and sees you. He shouts out an invitation for you to come round and have a drink and then goes back indoors. Do you still dump the offending faeces into his garden?

You have some friends coming around and you are just preparing to stage a party for some children in your garden. Do you now dump the offending faeces into your neighbour's garden?

 NO | YES   *Question ends* |

As you scoop up the mess, you hear your phone ring. Your neighbour's garden is the quickest and most convenient place to dump it on the way to answering the phone. Do you now dump the offending faeces into your neighbour's garden?

154

QUESTION 128

You are walking along the street when you notice a bracelet lying in the gutter. It looks quite expensive and you estimate that you could get about £50 for it. You are not hard up but neither are you rolling in money. The nearest police station is about half a mile away. Do you hand in the bracelet to the police?

YES

NO

As you pick it up and put it in your pocket, a woman who was nearby runs over and asks if you have just found her bracelet. She describes it fairly accurately but you know that she could well have seen this much from where she had been standing. She looks neither particularly well-off nor trustworthy. Do you still hand in the bracelet to the police rather than give it to this woman?

You've only gone a few more steps when you notice some make-up in the gutter. A bit further up you notice a notebook and then a handbag. It would seem that the bracelet and the other items have all come from the bag. The handbag does not look particularly expensive. There is identification in it and from the area in which they live you would guess that they are of moderate income. Do you now hand the bracelet in to the police?

YES | NO   *Question ends* |

She follows you frantically on the way to the police station. She explains that the bracelet was her first gift from her husband and has great sentimental value. However, he got it from a 'friend' at such a low price that they both suspected it was stolen property. She explains that if you hand it in she won't be able to claim it as she has no proof of purchase and the police might also identify it as stolen. It seems to mean a lot to her. Do you still take it to the police rather than give it to this woman?

NO | YES   *Question ends* |

The situation is the same, except that the handbag is rather tatty and contains a pension book. Do you now hand the bracelet in to the police?

QUESTION 129

You are at a friend's house some distance from your home when the phone rings. Your friend is busy and asks you to answer it. It turns out to be a frighteningly obscene call. Amazingly, you recognize the voice of your neighbour at home who has always been most civil and considerate to you although you are not close friends. Do you tell the police?

 YES

 NO

YES

The voice that you recognize on the phone is not your neighbour but that of your local vicar who would obviously suffer terribly from the revelation. Such a case could also attract the attention of the national press. Do you still tell the police?

NO

When you tell your friend what the call was, they are very distressed. They confess that they have already had several such calls and have been too frightened by them to go to the police. Knowing who the culprit is, do you go to the police?

 YES | NO   *Question ends* |

 NO | YES   *Question ends* |

Before you tell the police, you tell your friend. They laugh and say that they get the calls quite regularly and are never upset by them. Your friend seems to dismiss the whole thing as a bit of a joke that does no harm. Do you still tell the police?

In this instance, it also happens that members of your own household have been similarly distressed by obscene calls. Do you now go to the police?

QUESTION 130

You are completely broke and a friend lends you £10 to see you through to the end of the week. As it happens, you forget and your friend, knowing that you are short of cash, refrains from mentioning it. You remember a month later. Your friend has since returned to university 100 miles away. Do you promptly send them the £10 which you can just spare now?

 YES

 NO

For one reason or another, you end up slipping a £10 note into a letter to them. The next time you speak to your friend, they mention that you have not repaid them. They have obviously not received the letter which is now months overdue. You can just spare £10. Do you give them another £10?

You hear through a friend that the friend who lent you the money is hard up at the moment. However, they have never mentioned the money you owe them and have apparently forgotten about it. You know that you won't be seeing them in the near future. You can just spare £10. Do you now send it to them?

 YES | NO   *Question ends* |

 NO | YES   *Question ends* |

The same initial situation, except that the friend who lent you the £10 is not at university but in a very well-paid job. When they lent you the money, they said not to worry about paying it back. You can just spare £10. Do you pay them back?

You hear through another friend that the friend who lent you the money is very annoyed that you have not returned it. You can just spare £10. Do you now send it to them, whether with or without a note of excuse?

QUESTION 131

You are wandering home one night along a very small side-street that you seldom use. You happen to glance down a small alley. High up, you see the windows of a flat. The lights are on and the curtains are open. Suddenly, a naked person moves into view in one of the windows. They are of the opposite sex to you and from what you can see, which is virtually everything, they are very attractive. They seem occupied in doing something and are obviously unaware that they can be seen from the street. Do you pause and watch?

 YES

 NO

You see them wander around their rooms, often in full view through the window. Eventually, you wander home. This small seldom used side-street is not your usual route but is no longer than the route you normally take. When walking home another evening, do you choose now to use the side-street?

As they turn, you recognize the person. It is somebody you have often seen around the area. You have always found them extremely attractive and interesting. You would really like to meet them some time. Do you now pause and watch?

 YES | NO   *Question ends* |

You see this person naked in their window fairly regularly whenever you do. Although they never do anything deliberate or sexy, you definitely get the impression that they are intentionally exhibiting themselves. Do you still choose to take this route home?

 NO | YES   *Question ends* |

Just then another person moves into view. Somebody of the same sex as you. They are also naked. The couple in the window begin to embrace intimately. Their hands start to rove. Do you now pause and watch?

QUESTION 132

You are on holiday abroad. You meet a compatriot there who tells you that a 2p coin will operate some local vending machines instead of the necessary coin of that country which is worth about 10p. You happen to have some 2p coins with you in your bags. Do you then carry them around to use them in a vending machine in case you might want to buy something?

 YES

 NO

After wandering around, you find that there is nothing you actually want to buy from any vending machines. Before you return home, do you spend the 2p pieces in some machines anyway just because you can buy something so cheaply?

In this instance, the 2p coins operate the machines in place of a coin worth 50p. Do you now try to use the 2p pieces?

 YES | NO   *Question ends* |

NO | **YES**   *Question ends* |

In this instance, the coins came in useful in some machines for bus tickets, local cigarettes, etc. A year or so later, you are visiting the country in question. Before you go, do you deliberately visit the bank and get a few pounds' worth of 2p pieces specifically to take with you?

The compatriot tells you that there is also a local coin worth about 10p that will operate machines in place of a £1 coin back home. He adds that he always takes bags of them back and uses them on machines that give change such as on the London Tube. Do you make an effort to ensure that you take some of these coins back with you?

QUESTION 133

You have been asked to write a question for this book. You happen to know of a true-life problem that actually happened to an acquaintance of yours whom you no longer see very often. However, you know that should you present the problem in the book and that person were to read it they would immediately be able to identify themselves as the victim of the problem. From the facts presented, any friend of theirs would also be able to identify them. To present the problem would also reveal facts that only you and the victim know. The revelation of these would cause the person acute embarrassment. Do you present the problem for inclusion in this book?

 YES

In this instance, the problem involved a business acquaintance through whom you earn some money, though not much. To publish the problem would reveal that you do not have a very high regard for them or their opinions and could cost you their business which you need – just. In fact, it would reveal that you think them an absolute pig. Do you publish the problem?

 YES | **NO**   *Question ends* |

In this instance, the problem involves your closest friend. To publish it would definitely cause friction between them and their partner. Do you still publish this problem?

 NO

In this instance, the problem involved you. At the moment, if you published it, nobody would be able to identify you from the question. However, if at a later date, other facts become known, then your friends would be able to. This would cause you and only you some acute embarrassment. Would you publish this problem?

 NO | **YES**   *Question ends* |

In this instance, you heard the problem secondhand at a party and not from anyone you know. Nobody you know is concerned in the story and you do not know if the people involved could be identified from it nor whether it would cause them embarrassment if they were. Would you publish this problem?

QUESTION 134

You make an error at work that is certain to cost the company a great deal of money. However, the error is such that you know that no one will be able to trace it to you. Do you inform your superior of your error?

 YES

You are severely reprimanded and told that should you make the same mistake again, you could lose your job. Under severe pressure from personal problems, you make the same mistake again. It cannot be traced to you. Do you tell your superiors this time?

 YES | **NO**   *Question ends* |

You lose your job. After some time you find another job with a different company. However, the break between jobs has strained your personal finances to the limit. While getting used to the working systems with the new company, you make a similar mistake. Again, it cannot be traced to you. Do you tell your new superiors?

 NO

The error causes considerable concern. There is a colleague you do not particularly like and who is unpopular with the management. Your superiors think that this person is responsible for the error. The suspect is worried since they have been reprimanded before and could well lose their job this time. Do you now tell your superiors that the error was yours?

 NO | **YES**   *Question ends* |

Your superiors have spoken to the suspect and are now convinced that they were not the person responsible for the mistake. They now seem sure that it was your best friend in the office. Your best friend has been reprimanded before and could lose their job this time. Do you now tell your superiors the truth?

QUESTION 135

You have gone with a group of friends in a car to a festival of some kind. You are about 150 miles from home. After going your separate ways at the festival you meet back at the car. The driver, whom you only know through some of your close friends in the group, is obviously a little the worse for drink, as are the other drivers in the group. You do not or cannot drive at the moment. The driver insists that he is well capable of driving the 150 miles back home. All the others are going back in the car. You have enough money to catch a train. There is a station nearby and you know that the trains are still running. Do you go back with the others in the car?

 YES

 NO

En route, the others fall asleep in the back. You are in the front with the driver. It soon becomes apparent to you that his driving is dangerous. He has bumped over the grass verge on several occasions and veered about the road slightly. You have only gone about fifteen miles when he stops for some fresh air in the next town. The others wake up. They do not know what has happened. There is a station in the town. Trains are still running. The others are all continuing by car and nobody else will drive. Do you still continue your journey in the car?

The situation is the same, except that it is fairly late and you do not know whether the trains are still running. Do you go back with the others in the car?

 NO

YES *Question ends*

It is very late and raining. You don't have enough money on you for the train fare, nor do you have any credit cards or other means of paying. You would have to hitch-hike back as there is no alternative. Do you go back with the others in the car?

 YES

NO *Question ends*

At this point one of the others decides that they would rather go back by train and proceeds to do so. Do you still continue by car?

QUESTION 136

You have a close friend whom you have always known to be a bit of a rogue. They have often been involved in money-making schemes, sometimes on the fringes of legality, usually to no avail as they are continually broke. You hugely enjoy their company as they are really entertaining and their hare-brained schemes have often had hilarious results. However, your friend suddenly seems to be quite well off. He tells you that he has been doing some odd jobs that turned out quite lucrative. When he buys a brand-new car with cash, you begin to wonder. Then, one day at your local pub, you hear a rumour that he has been selling drugs to some of the customers, though the rumour does not say which drugs. Do you mind your own business rather than ask your friend or go to the police?

 YES   **NO**

YES column:

Your friend seems to have more and more money to hand. You read in your local paper reports of a growing heroin problem among teenagers in your area. Do you continue to mind your own business rather than ask your friend or go to the police?

 YES | **NO**   *Question ends* |

You are in a pub one evening. As you go to the toilets out at the back, you see your friend apparently selling something to a teenage girl in the shadows of the yard. Do you still continue to mind your own business rather than ask your friend or go to the police?

NO column:

You talk to your friend, who denies dealing in drugs. He claims to have been doing odd jobs for some wealthy Arabs. However, a few days later while going to the toilets out at the back of your local pub, you see your friend selling something to a teenage girl in the shadows of the yard. You glimpse a sachet of white powder. They haven't seen you and both leave through the back gate. Do you now mind your own business rather than go to the police?

NO | **YES**   *Question ends* |

The same situation, except that when you see your friend in the yard the packet he is selling is dark in colour. He sees you and laughs. The girl slips out of the back gate. He comes over and says, 'OK. So you caught me red-handed. I'm making a bit of money selling grass.' He shows you some more similar packets in his pocket. Do you now mind your own business rather than go to the police?

QUESTION 137

You are alone in your car driving through a built-up area one fine evening. Suddenly, a cat darts in front of your car and is run over. A quick glance tells you that the poor thing is certainly dead. There is nothing that you could have done to prevent the accident. There is nobody around. Do you stop at least to pay your last respects to the unfortunate feline?

 YES

 NO

In this instance, you were driving along in the countryside. The animal that you've just run over and killed was a rabbit. Do you still stop?

At this instant, you notice a little girl in a doorway. The cat had been running towards her. Now do you stop?

 YES

 | NO   *Question ends* |

Still in the countryside, except that the animal that you have just run over and killed was a rat. Do you now stop?

 NO

| **YES**   *Question ends* |

The girl shouts through the door behind her and a man appears, her father. They are evidently the owners of the cat. The man runs to the pavement and waves at your car. He is near enough to be able to take your number. Do you now stop?

QUESTION 138

You have been on holiday in Norway. In a small coastal fishing town, you have become extremely friendly with the family of a local fishing-boat captain. So much so, that when he suggests that you extend your holiday because he will be taking his boat across to Scotland soon and could drop you off, you accept the invitation. After spending a very enjoyable few weeks in the family home, you set off. The crossing is pleasant and comfortable and the captain takes the opportunity to do some trawling *en route*. Just off the Scottish coast, the net brings up a sealed barrel with the markings of an American chemical company on the side as well as a lot of dead fish and marine creatures. The captain tells you that it is illegal for him to fish in Scottish waters and that he could be fined several thousand pounds if caught. He feels that what the British dump off their own coast is their own business. However, he adds that if you wish to report the incident, he'll not dump the barrel back in the sea but drop it ashore somewhere for you to hand over to the authorities. He asks you, however, to keep his name out of it. Do you decide to report the incident, in one way or another, to the authorities?

YES

After being dropped in a small town, you buy a paper. A small news item catches your eye. Under an agreement between Britain and Norway just ratified, illegal fishing within territorial waters can result in a lifetime ban. You know that fishing is your new-found friend's life. Do you still report the incident, one way or another, to the authorities?

YES | NO   *Question ends*

You report the incident. However, on investigation the barrel does not contain toxic wastes but the authorities are still interested because of your report of the dead fish in the area. They need to know precisely where the barrel was found. The only one who could tell them this is the captain of the boat. Do you give the authorities his name?

NO

You're dropped off in a nearby port. It is late and there is no transport until morning so you must stay overnight. In the pub, you learn that the area is a major centre for the production of smoked fish for the UK market. The fish are all caught locally. Do you now, in one way or another, report the incident to the authorities?

NO | YES   *Question ends*

Still in the pub, you later become engaged in a conversation with the local doctor. He tells you of the increasing number of malformed babies being born in the area. He had formerly put the occasional instance down as the result of years of in-breeding. However, over recent years the numbers have increased dramatically and he is concerned. Do you now, in one way or another, report the incident?

QUESTION 139

A relative dies and leaves you some shares in a company. You are not desperate for money and the shares are extremely lucrative ones. However, the company is involved in the manufacture of chemical herbicides. At the moment, the shares are not well priced for selling; to do so would lose money. Do you sell your shares in this company immediately rather than hold on to them?

 YES

 NO

The same situation, except that in a recent environmentalist report the company was praised. Though not considered perfect, it was adjudged to be the only one in its field that was actually conducting research into potentially safer alternatives, had extremely high standards of safety procedure, involved itself in debates and took into consideration the views of environmental organizations. Do you still sell your shares in this company immediately?

You read in the paper of a disastrous accident in a third-world country. A storage vat in a chemical herbicide works was destroyed in a fire causing many deaths and polluting the surrounding countryside. More deaths and illnesses are anticipated in the affected area. The plant was part of the company in which you hold shares. They are not well priced for selling. Do you now sell the shares immediately?

 NO

YES Question ends

 YES

NO Question ends

You next read that the company has won a lucrative military contract with both your government and the American government. It is widely assumed that the contract is for chemical warfare agents. The shares are underpriced at the moment but are guaranteed to rise in the near future because of these contracts. Do you, however, sell them immediately?

The same situation, except that all you know, or can find out about the company at the moment, is that it manufactures chemicals of some kind. You have no idea what type or what for. Do you still sell the shares immediately?

QUESTION 140

You find yourself at a large, specially organized social gathering. Also present is a well-known political figure whose views you find totally repellent. This person is being introduced to people near you. The group then moves on to you. One of the organizers introduces you and the politician proffers a hand. Do you shake hands with this person?

YES

NO

YES — The same situation, except that an election is imminent. As the handshake is offered, a group of local and national photographers congregate around you. It is obvious that the occasion is being used as part of a publicity drive by the politician. The photographers have their cameras at the ready. Do you still shake hands with the politician?

NO — At that moment, a dear friend appears next to you. They have, misguidedly you think, helped to organize the gathering. You know that they will be very embarrassed, even compromised, by any unpleasantness. Do you now shake the hand proffered by the politician?

NO | **YES** *Question ends*

YES | **NO** *Question ends*

The same situation, the photographers are gathered, except that you learned that morning that the politician was instrumental in organizing a violent confrontation with their opponents in which people had been badly injured, including a friend of yours. Do you still shake the politician's hand?

The same situation, except that you have encountered this politician before. On that occasion, on hearing your views, they had rudely sworn 'never even to shake the hand of the likes of you'. They obviously don't recall this. Regardless of whether you intend to mention this, do you now shake their hand?

QUESTION 141

Christmas is coming, the geese are getting fat, but you're rushing around trying to buy presents. There are only a few days left and you still have several to buy. You will be spending Christmas at the home of some close friends. They have an eight-year-old daughter. You must buy her a present. You have asked what she wants and have been told that what she is asking for is a Girlie World – a make-up set that comes with a model girl's head to which the make-up is applied. Your friends have no objection to this. Do you choose to buy the Girlie World for the child?

 YES

 NO

This time, it is the girl herself who has told you that the Girlie World is what she really, really wants more than anything. You do not know whether the parents approve or not. Do you still choose to buy the Girlie World?

 YES | NO   *Question ends*

Once again, the girl has told you that she wants the Girlie World, but this time you know that the parents disapprove of what they refer to as role-model toys. They would never buy such a toy for the girl themselves. Do you still choose to buy the Girlie World?

The girl also mentioned something else that she wanted. This is a lifelike baby doll that you feed with some special gunk. The baby then burps, vomits and messes in its nappy. Time is running out, you have only one day left and you have so far seen nothing else that you thought would be suitable. Do you now buy the Girlie World for the girl?

NO | YES   *Question ends*

It is now Christmas Eve. Just a few more shopping hours left. You are desperate. Everything worthwhile seems to have disappeared from the shops. All that remains is the Girlie World that the girl wants and a road safety game that looks rather dreary and uninspired. There is no time left to look any further. Do you now buy the Girlie World?

QUESTION 142

It is a cold, wet, winter's night. On your way home from a restaurant, you find a small dog shivering in a doorway. It is soaked and showing signs of neglect. It looks at you and gives a small whimper. It has a collar on but there is no name or address attached to it. Do you take the dog home with the intention of keeping it?

 YES

 NO

The little dog is very affectionate and soon becomes part of the family. One month later, you notice an advertisement in the window of the local newsagent that describes the dog perfectly and asks for the return of 'the much-loved family pet'. Do you neglect to answer the advertisement and keep the dog?

 YES | **NO** *Question ends*

While you are walking the dog in the local park, a little girl sees it and runs up to it calling it by name. The dog is obviously delighted to see her, wagging its tail and licking her hand. She is scruffy and obviously from a poor home. She asks for her dog back. Do you still insist on keeping the dog?

For some reason the dog follows you, trotting shyly behind you. You reach home. The dog is still there and it is still raining, so you decide to take it in for the night, intending to find it a home or take it to the RSPCA. Nobody you know wants the dog, but you notice a sign in the local newsagent's window that describes the dog perfectly and asks for the return of 'the much-loved family pet'. You inform the family and the man comes to collect the dog. He enquires where the 'little bastard' is and says that it is always running away. As soon as he gets it home, he is going to give it a thrashing that will put a stop to 'that kind of behaviour in a hurry'. Do you keep the dog rather than hand it over to this man?

 NO | **YES** *Question ends*

The dog won't go near the man and even snaps at him when he tries to touch it. The man swears at it and goes off saying, 'You can have the little sod.' There is now only the dogs' home left. You take the dog there.

A short time later a friend tells you that an acquaintance of theirs at the dogs' home has said that no one has claimed it and that it will shortly be put down. Do you go and claim the dog?

QUESTION 143

You are at work. You are conducting a stranger around showing them various aspects of the business – a student whom nobody knows but who has been given permission to look around as part of their studies. They praise a piece of the work they see as brilliant and ask if you did it. You did not. The person who did it is no longer with the company. Do you say, or try to give the impression, that the work is in fact yours?

 YES

 NO

A new person joins the company as your superior. They praise some past work describing it as brilliant, and ask if you were responsible for it. You were not. The person who did it is still with the company, and you know them. Do you say, or try to give the impression, that the work is yours?

 YES | NO   *Question ends* |

The same situation, except that the person who did the work has given you due credit in the past in a similar situation. However, you do not know them except by name. Do you still say, or try to give the impression, that the work is yours?

A superior has left the company and there is a promotion in the offing. It is a position that you really want. The 'high-ups' are interviewing you and some other colleagues for the position. In the course of your interview, they produce some past work and praise it, saying that it displays just the qualities for which they are looking. They say that they believe the work to be yours and ask you to confirm this. You did not do it, but the person who did it has left the company. Only you know who did do the work. Do you say, or try to give the impression, that the work is yours?

 NO | YES   *Question ends* |

The situation is the same, except that the person who did the work is still with the company and is a rival for the promotion. They have not been spoken to yet and happen to be the person you hate most in the company. If you take the credit now, the issue will obviously not be raised by your high-ups with that person and no one would be the wiser. Do you say, or try to give the impression, that the work is yours?

QUESTION 144

You are in London riding on the Tube. There is a young girl, respectably dressed, sitting opposite you. Seated next to her is a respectably dressed business man. It is a double seat. Suddenly the girl screams at the man, 'Get your filthy hands off me, you bastard!' The man is looking shocked and embarrassed. The girl is obviously angry. You have not seen what happened as you were reading a paper. Do you join the girl in reprimanding the man or, at least, give silent moral support to her?

 YES

 NO

The man gets up and rather shamefacedly gets off at the next station. Another man gets on and sits beside the girl. You are reading your paper, when suddenly exactly the same thing happens again. Once again, you have seen nothing happen as you were not watching. Do you still give your moral support to the girl?

 YES

| NO   *Question ends* |

This man gets off and another gets on and sits beside the girl. You are watching this time. Nothing happens but the girl does the same thing again. The man goes and another gets on. The only empty seat is the one beside the girl. He is going to sit there. Do you do nothing rather than try in any way to warn *him*?

You are on the Tube again but this time the girl is sitting a few seats along from you. The man is seated directly opposite her. He is staring at her and under cover of a newspaper has his hand in his pocket and is playing with himself, making sure that the girl knows what he is doing. She is acutely embarrassed and flustered. You are the only one other than the girl who can see that is happening. Do you now reprimand the man?

 NO

| YES   *Question ends* |

The man now actually exposes himself to the girl under cover of the newspaper. She is obviously too embarrassed and frightened to say anything. You are the only other person aware of what is happening. Do you now reprimand the man?

QUESTION 145

You are working as the head of a small department within a large company. This company is taken over by a large conglomerate. The new directors demand a drive for profitability, which means redundancies. You must dismiss one person from your department. Everybody in your department, save one, has been with the company since it started and has worked hard to build up the company. However, you dislike one member intensely – but they happen to be one of the best workers. The fairest decision would be to sack the last person to join. This is a forty-five-year-old man with a wife, mortgage and three kids. He is just managing to keep his head above water and at his age may have terrible problems getting another job. He works hard but is the least efficient of your workers, though not by much, simply because he has not been there as long and the others know the business inside out. Nobody volunteers for the sack so you must choose. Do you sack the forty-five-year-old man?

 YES   **NO**

He comes into your office and pleads for his job. He points out that he is learning fast and you could sack one of the others who, though they've been there longer, are all younger, have fewer commitments and more chance of finding another job. Do you still stick to your decision?

When the directors hear of your decision, they do not agree. They point out that the forty-five-year-old is the ideal man to get rid of. They suggest you rethink your decision. Do you now give him the sack?

 NO   ⟍ | **YES**   *Question ends* |

 YES | NO   *Question ends* |

The next day, his wife rings. She is in tears and is terrified as to what the job loss will mean to them. She is breaking down on the phone. Do you still stick to your decision?

The new directors are not happy with you. They think that your decisions are influenced by your emotions rather than the practicalities of what is best for the company. Your future is in jeopardy. They suggest that you think again, intimating that if the forty-five-year-old doesn't go, you will. Do you now give him the sack?

QUESTION 146

You receive a chain-letter from one of the other people with whom you are playing this game. It is the sort of letter that asks you to send off £1 to a name at the top of the list, add your name to the bottom and then send copies of the list on to five other friends of yours. The letter promises that you will make a lot of money. However, apart from the person who sent you the letter, you know none of the other eleven names on the list. Do you break the chain?

 YES

 NO

The person who sent you the letter asserts that they have direct knowledge of someone who made a three-figure sum out of such a chain-letter. Do you still break the chain?

The list is very long, over twenty names. Now do you break the chain?

 YES

| NO   *Question ends* |

The list, in this instance, is quite short and you know virtually all the other people on it, either as friends or acquaintances. Do you still break the chain?

 NO

| YES   *Question ends* |

You've just read a newspaper article about such letters. They are illegal and the article reported that many people are in fact photocopying the letter hundreds of times and sending it out to names and addresses from telephone directories. Do you now break the chain?

QUESTION 147

You are strolling home alone late at night in the summer. It is dark and deserted. You are passing along a road that is brightly lit but has dark areas of heathland on either side. Suddenly, you hear the brief scream of a woman. All is silent again. You could not tell whether the scream was of fright, fun, or what, but it came from a large clump of bushes about fifty yards on to the heathland. Do you go to investigate?

YES | **NO**

You stealthily approach the bushes. In the moonlight, you can just make out what appears to be a couple making love on the ground. To get nearer, you would have to enter the bushes and would certainly make some noise that would alert them to your presence. Do you approach further to find out if anything is wrong?

You are proceeding on your way when you hear a woman's voice again. It sounds like a muffled shout for help, though you can't be sure. The nearest call box is about fifteen minutes away. Once again, the sound emanated from the same clump of bushes. Do you now go and investigate?

 YES | **NO** *Question ends*

NO | **YES** *Question ends*

As you do so, you disturb the bushes. A man's voice calls out, 'Who's there?' You hear a woman's muffled whimpers. The man calls out, 'One step nearer, and I'll cut her. I've got a knife.' You know the nearest house or call box is about fifteen minutes away. Do you stay put in the hope of frightening the man off before he can do anything more to the woman?

The air is pierced again by the woman's voice. This time it is a definite scream for help. You also recognize the voice as that of a friend of yours who lives near here. Do you now go and investigate?

QUESTION 148

You are on your first date with someone you find really attractive. As you sit down at a table for two in an isolated corner of a restaurant, embarrassingly but silently you fart. Do you pretend that nothing has happened rather than admit it?

 YES   **NO**

Your date begins to shift uneasily in their chair. They turn their head a little and sniff the air in a slightly puzzled way. You can also smell it quite strongly. Do you still pretend that nothing has happened rather than admit it?

Your new date is not particularly impressed with your honesty, obviously finding it a little vulgar. Just then, another silent fart slides out and you begin to regret trying the baked Jerusalem artichokes at lunchtime. The previous one is still lingering on the air. Do you pretend that nothing has happened rather than admit that you've done it again?

 YES | NO   *Question ends* |

Your date, after a few muttered noises, asks you if you've farted. Do you deny, or avoid, the question rather than admit it?

NO | YES   *Question ends* |

You can feel the Jerusalem artichokes working their mischief as your stomach grumbles quietly to itself. You realize that this side effect will be occurring regularly through the evening. Do you politely disappear to the toilet at convenient intervals rather than explain the situation and stay put?

QUESTION 149

There is a scrappy, untidy tree in your garden that definitely needs to be cut down. You've wanted to do it for ages and, now, today is the day. When you approach it to cut it down, you see a nest and a mother bird sitting on it. She is startled by your approach, but stays on the nest. Do you now cut the tree down?

YES

As you begin to cut the tree, the bird panics and flies off to another nearby tree. You can hear a chorus of cheeps. Looking up, you see several young chicks poking their heads out from the nest. They are obviously still too young to fly. Do you continue to cut the tree down?

YES | NO   *Question ends* |

Just then the cock bird arrives. This bird is startlingly coloured. You realize that it is quite rare and remember reading in your local paper that such a bird had been sighted in the area. Do you still continue to cut down the tree?

NO

This looks like the bird that has been waking you early every morning with raucous calls from your window sill. What's more, it has also terrorized the smaller birds that come to your garden for nuts and scraps. Do you now cut the tree down?

NO | YES   *Question ends* |

You lean against the tree to look at the nest better, As you do, the tree gives slightly. It is clearly in a dangerous state and the next high wind will probably bring it crashing on to the garden fence for which you are responsible. This will involve you in time and expense repairing the fence. Do you now cut the tree down?

QUESTION 150

You have been involved in some charity work that has proved very successful. So successful that it has attracted royal patronage. As a result, you, along with the others concerned in the charity work, have been invited to a special function at Buckingham Palace in support of, and to help publicize, the cause for which you have been working. This is in two days' time. You are looking for some suitable clothes to wear for the occasion. While shopping, you find exactly what you want. However, the only one of your size is in the shop window. Before the assistant can get it for you, another assistant removes it for someone else to try on whom it suits perfectly. However, they seem very indecisive. You are the only other customer there. They turn to you in a friendly manner and ask your opinion. You think that the clothes suit them perfectly. However, this is also the only thing that you have seen so far that you like and suits your needs. Do you tell them that the clothes suit them?

 YES

 NO

As you are about to answer, the person glances out of the shop window and gesticulates. Outside, you can see their chauffeur waiting next to a Rolls-Royce stacked to the roof with packages from similar clothes shops. Do you still tell them that you think the clothes suit them?

 YES | NO   *Question ends* |

The same situation, except that the person with the Rolls-Royce has not asked your opinion in a friendly manner. It was more of an order for you to give your opinion. Do you still tell them that you think the clothes suit them?

As they proceed to ask your opinion, you realize the cause of their apparent indecisiveness: they have a very bad stammer. They hesitatingly ask you for your opinion. Do you now tell them you think the clothes suit them?

 NO | YES   *Question ends* |

The same situation, except that the person does not have a stammer. Instead, before you can answer, you notice a white stick beside their bags on the floor. You realize that the person is asking your opinion because they are blind. Do you tell them that the clothes suit them?

QUESTION 151

You are seriously ill. After a visit to the doctor, you are rushed to hospital. There you are told that your condition is severe and could eventually prove fatal. However, the condition can be treated in one of two ways. You can take a course of treatment which will take a long time and could cause you some pain and discomfort. Or, alternatively, you could take a short series of injections of a new serum. However, the serum has had much publicity recently from anti-vivisectionists as it was developed with the aid of some particularly horrendous experimentation on live animals. The doctor recommends that you take the serum but leaves the choice to you. Do you take the serum?

 YES   **NO**

The same situation, except that you know that the serum was developed as the result of experimentation on live human test-tube foetuses, which are also used in its manufacture. Do you still decide to take this new serum?

 YES | NO   *Question ends*

There is a demonstration at the hospital against the use of the serum. You were unaware that you are one of the first people to be treated with it and this received some local publicity. Now, you are to be interviewed for television. You realize that if you decide to go ahead with the series of injections it will receive considerable national attention with a body of public opinion against you. Do you still decide to take the serum?

You take the alternative course of treatment and it does result in considerable pain. In fact, you are in agony. However, the doctor says that though it seems to be paying dividends the course will still be a long one and the pain will continue for some time, maybe months. Do you now decide to take the serum?

 NO | YES   *Question ends*

The doctor tells you that the course seems to have had some effect, but no more. It would be useless to continue. He tells you that unless you now take the serum, your chances of survival would be 60 per cent. Any decision must be made now; to take the serum later would be useless. Do you now decide to take the serum?

QUESTION 152

It is your mother's birthday tomorrow. You have bought an expensive coffee-table book which she has been asking for repeatedly for some months. You take it home. Unfortunately, as you prepare to wrap it, you drop it and tear one of the pages. The shop had plenty of other copies of the book when you bought it. Do you return the book claiming that it was sold damaged in order to get a replacement or a refund?

YES

In this instance, you did not tear a page. Instead, you spilt some coffee over some of the beautiful full-page colour illustrations in such a way that it would be impossible to claim that the book was in that condition when you bought it. You still have the receipt and the shop's bag. Do you go back to the shop with the book to switch it slyly for an undamaged copy?

 YES   NO   *Question ends*

Once again, you have torn a page rather than spilt coffee over the book. However, when you bought the book you had great difficulty in finding a copy. It is out of print. You searched through many bookshops before finding just one copy in a small back-street shop. It is Saturday afternoon and only two hours before the shops close. Do you still take the book back claiming that it was sold damaged to get a refund?

NO

In this instance, when you dropped the book, you did not tear a page – or were not aware if you did. A little later as you are thumbing through, you discover a ripped page. It could have been done when you dropped the book, on the other hand it could have been like it when you bought the book. You have no idea. Do you now take the book back claiming that it was sold damaged to get a replacement or a refund?

 NO   YES   *Question ends*

As you close the book, you notice a blank page. You check to find that this copy has been misprinted. There are several blank pages. You have still torn a page. Do you now take the book back in order to get a replacement or a refund?

QUESTION 153

You are queuing to buy a train ticket. You have plenty of time. When the middle-aged couple in front of you reach the ticket office, it becomes clear that they are tourists and do not speak the language very well. They ask for their tickets and the clerk tells them the price. They rummage in their pockets and bags, look hard at the various coins and place some money on the counter. They are 20p short. The clerk is particularly unhelpful and simply looks at them and repeats the price. The couple look puzzled and simply shuffle the money on the counter around and look at the clerk who continues to repeat the price in a bad-tempered way. You are in no hurry and do not speak their language. Do you stand idly by while all this is going on?

YES

NO

The situation is the same, except that your train is due to leave shortly. Do you stand by, either idly or impatiently, rather than do anything to help the couple?

You try to explain the problem to them, but they still do not seem to understand. Eventually, you realize that they are on their way out of the country and this is all the loose change they have. They have some notes but were hoping not to have to change them for coins as they would then be unable to change them back into their own currency. Do you continue to explain that they need to change a note as they are 20p short rather than make up their fare with 20p from your own pocket?

YES | NO   *Question ends* |

The situation is the same, except that it is not a middle-aged couple but a flustered old lady. Do you still stand by unhelpfully?

NO | YES   *Question ends* |

The situation is the same, except that the tourists are rather arrogant and unfriendly people whose attitude has caused the clerk to be so unhelpful. Would you now stand idly by?

QUESTION 154

You are very hard up and out of work. You hear through a friend that you can earn some money as a human guinea pig. Apparently, drug companies are willing to pay people to take a course of a drug just prior to its release on the market. The drugs have already been exhaustively tested and this procedure is just a final safeguard. At one such company, the pay is £50 per week. All you have to do is take some pills and report in once a week. Do you decide to do this?

 YES

 NO

After a while on one course, you notice that your hair is starting to fall out. Not dramatically, but it is thinning noticeably. When you report this at your check-up at the drug company, you are told not to worry as this is a side effect of which the company was aware. You are told that the hair loss is only temporary and that it soon grows back once the course stops. Do you continue to act as a guinea pig?

You find another company where they pay £100 per week for the same type of work. Do you now decide to work as a guinea pig?

 NO | **YES**   *Question ends* |

A friend who has taken up the work tells you that the company is looking for people to test a drug that has been developed. This drug is believed to be a breakthrough in the fight against a particular illness of which there happens to be a history in your family. Do you now decide to work as a guinea pig?

 YES | **NO**   *Question ends* |

Your hair grows back. You are now taking a different course. You find that you are losing your desire for sex. When you report this, the company is obviously surprised at this side effect. Do you still continue to work as a guinea pig?

QUESTION 155

There is a transport strike on. There are no trains and few buses. You have no car and must therefore catch a bus to get to work. While you are waiting for the bus, a stranger stops in his car and asks if anyone in the queue wants a lift. It happens that he is going to where your work is. Some others in the queue get into the back of the car. As you get into the front passenger seat, you notice a £10 note stuck under it. During the journey, do you quietly slip it into your pocket?

YES

NO

The situation is the same, except that it is a good friend of yours giving you the lift. Do you still slip the £10 note into your pocket?

YES | **NO**   *Question ends*

The same situation, except that it is your lover giving you the lift. Do you still slip the £10 note into your pocket without saying anything?

You are in the country. Somehow you have become stranded and the only way to get back to the town where you are to catch a train is to hitch-hike. You do this and to your amazement, a Rolls-Royce stops to give you a lift. Once again, you notice a £10 note caught under the seat as you get in. Do you slip it quietly into your pocket during the journey?

NO | **YES**   *Question ends*

On another occasion, you ring for a minicab to get home from a party. The cab arrives. As you get in you find a £10 note caught under the seat. Do you quietly slip it into your pocket?

QUESTION 156

You are with some friends in a pub. In the corner sits a strange-looking woman. She is wrapped in dirty and faded clothing that was once brightly coloured. She has dark hair and wild eyes. She looks gypsyish. Later, she comes to your table and speaks to you. She wants to read your palm. Somebody else pipes up that they want theirs read but she refuses. She wants to read yours and only yours because, 'You look interesting.' Others offer to pay but she adds that she wants no money. She only wants to read your palm. Do you let her?

YES ———————————————— **NO**

She looks closely at your palm, rubbing her fingers across the surface of your hand. She looks up at you, her eyes gleaming. She begins to tell you of some past events in your life, vague at first but applicable. Then she begins to tell you more specific things with surprising accuracy. Regardless of whether you are sceptical, you are impressed. Then she looks you straight in the eye. She tells you that she can see misfortune ahead, grave misfortune. She says that she can tell you what it is likely to be and roughly when it might happen, but only if you want her to tell you. Do you want her to tell you?	She laughs. Leaning towards you, she says, 'A shame, my friend, for you have an interesting future. But beware! I have seen enough to tell that in a few years you will have an accident or illness. Nothing serious, but something that will be with you for the rest of your life. So take care.' With that she leaves the pub. Two years later, you slip and tear some ligaments in your knee. The doctors tell you that it will always be weak and to take care with it. Some time after this, you are in the pub again. The woman is there. She recognizes you and asks to read your palm again. Do you now let her?

YES | NO   *Question ends* | **NO** | YES   *Question ends* |

She tells you that one of your children will die young, probably in an accident or from an illness. She then adds that she can see your death. She asks if you want to know how and when you are likely to die. Do you want her to tell you this?	The original situation, except the woman does not look wild and mysterious. She is reading the palms of anyone who'll pay her 20p. You hear her readings of others. She is very funny and the whole thing is obviously a joke. She volunteers to read yours for 20p. Do you let her read your palm?

QUESTION 157

Your country is involved in a war in the Far East, much the same, and for the same reasons, as the Vietnam War. There is conscription. However, students at university or college are exempt. It is exam time. Students who pass their exams will be able to continue their courses. Those who fail will not be able to resit as they will receive their call-up papers for service in the war by the same post as their exam results. You know this as you happen to be an external examiner since you are an expert in the field in which you normally work. You are obliged by law to notify the authorities of all exam results before you notify the students. You are marking the exam papers knowing that those you fail will be off to fight in the war. Do you consequently shade up the marking, so that those who would normally have failed by the smallest whisker now pass?

 YES   **NO**

You realize that this will not be enough. Many students have actually done worse than they should have probably due to the additional pressures of this exam. Do you increase the marking to pass as many as you reasonably can without arousing any undue suspicion?

You can see that the normal exam nerves have been amplified by the problem of conscription. Practically all the students have underachieved in the exam. Many who should have passed have just failed. Do you now shade up the markings rather than mark the exams by the book?

 YES | **NO** *Question ends* | **NO** | **YES** *Question ends* |

The situation is the same, except that this is the first time you have ever acted as an external examiner. Your work may be vetted, you don't know. You do know that random checks are often held. If your marking is vetted and you are found to have upgraded students, you will lose your post. You will then be eligible for conscription and will receive your call-up papers. Do you still upgrade the students' marks, even by the slightest margin?

One of the students' names rings a bell. It is the relative of a friend of yours. You know that this particular family has already lost one child in service in the war. You can see that the student would normally have passed, but due to nerves should actually just fail this time. Do you mark up this student?

QUESTION 158 (non-vegetarian)

You host a large dinner party for about fifteen friends. One of the couples is vegetarian. For them, you prepare a vegetarian dish. For all the others you prepare a beautiful piece of roast lamb that you bought from the local family butcher where you frequently shop. The dinner goes well. However, during the night you are taken violently ill with vomiting and diarrhoea. You have a sleepless night, but by morning, it has cleared up and you feel OK again. During the course of the next morning, you learn that all the other guests who ate the meat have suffered similarly. The only two unaffected were the two vegetarians. The only food eaten by all those who were ill was the meat. You still have a small portion of it left. Do you go straight back to the butcher and complain?

 YES

 NO

The butcher is very apologetic and assures you that he gets his meat in fresh every day and takes the utmost precautions. He is convinced that there can have been nothing wrong with the meat. However, to show good faith he gives you a very large and expensive leg of lamb. Do you pursue the matter by taking the remaining meat to the health department for testing?

Do you take the remaining portion of meat to the health department for testing?

 NO | **YES   Question ends** |

 YES | **NO   Question ends** |

They test it and find nothing wrong with it. However, you now hear from the vegetarians that they had a stomach virus shortly before the dinner party with the same symptoms as you and the other guests suffered from. You also hear from other guests that people in their households who were not at the dinner have since gone down with the same bug. It was obviously a virus and not the meat. Do you take the leg of lamb back to the butcher and offer your apologies?

Two of the guests were your partner's parents. They are extremely pernickety and house-proud. You hear, through your partner, that they have put the illness down to your sloppy habits in the kitchen and are anti-you at the moment. You previously had a good relationship with them. Do you now do something about the meat to clear your name?

QUESTION 159

You're travelling in a taxi by yourself. The taxi driver is verbose and it soon becomes clear that he holds diametrically opposite views on politics to yourself. What's more he becomes pretty strident about it once he realizes where your sympathies lie. When you reach your destination, he says, 'All right. Get out!' This comes across as a genuine piece of incivility. Do you tip the taxi driver?

 YES

 NO

You only have a large note. As you are waiting for your change, you ask him for a particular direction. He ignores your inquiry although he must have heard. He gives you your change. Do you now tip him?

In this instance, the taxi driver is clearly an old codger, what you might describe as a London character. He's actually more grumpy than insulting. Now would you tip him?

 YES

| NO   *Question ends* |

NO

| **YES**   *Question ends* |

The taxi driver has clearly taken against you in a big way. Having given you your change, he immediately says, 'The only reason I take your filthy money is so's I can eat.' Do you now tip him?

In your dudgeon, you actually give him £1 too much for the fare. Without any edge, he tells you you've given him too much and hands a pound back. Do you now tip him?

QUESTION 160

You are in a clothes shop. There is a sale on. You find a suit at half price that you really like. The normal price would be more than you can afford, so you are excited by this bargain. When you go into the changing-room to try it on, you find that the jacket of one size fits perfectly but the trousers do not. However, the trousers of a different size fit perfectly. The mixed jacket and trousers are ideal and you would like to buy them. From the nature of the shop and the sale signs, you suspect that they will not allow you to mix the suits in this way. Do you try to buy the mixed suit rather than ask the assistant if this is possible?

YES

As you are about to leave the changing-room with the suits carefully switched, you hear another customer ask the assistant whether they have the suit in one of the sizes you have. You hear the assistant say that there is one, but somebody has it in the changing-room at the moment. Do you proceed with your intention to purchase the mixed suit hoping the other customer won't realize until you are out of the shop rather than ask whether you can mix the suits or sort them back into their correctly sized pairings?

YES | NO   Question ends |

You give the second mixed suit to the other customer and rush to the cash desk. The assistant has just rung up the price and you are about to pay when the other customer pops their head out of the changing-room and says, 'Excuse me, you must have got the sizes mixed up when you were putting them back on the hangers.' She brings over the suit she has. The assistant checks them and agrees. She sorts the suits back into their correct sizes. They both obviously assume you did this accidentally. However, the assistant now asks you which size it was you had wished to buy. Do you continue your purchase knowing that half the suit won't fit, or try to talk your way out of it, rather than ask if you can mix the sizes?

NO

You enquire if it is possible to switch the jackets and trousers of two different sizes. You are told that you may, but not in the sale. If you wish to do this, you must pay full price for the suit. You cannot really afford this. As you are walking back to replace the suit on the rack, the assistant goes off for coffee and a different one takes their place. They are not aware that you wished to switch jackets on the suits. Do you now try to switch the sizes and hope that it will not be noticed?

NO | YES   Question ends |

As you put your suits back on the rack, you notice a mixed suit there in the sizes you want. Somebody has already mixed some sizes. Regardless of whether you point this out to the assistant first, do you now try to buy this suit at the sale price?

QUESTION 161

You have a bad, persistent cough, which is loud and uncontrollable. No medicine seems to help. Other than that you feel OK. You have booked expensive seats at the theatre for a dramatic production that you are very keen to see. The play is due to run for quite some time. Your tickets are for tomorrow and your cough shows no sign of easing. Do you go to the show tomorrow night anyway?

YES

NO

A friend of yours is in the cast of the play. Do you still go on the night you have booked?

YES

| NO   *Question ends* |

Not only is a friend of yours in the cast but this also happens to be the opening night. You have complimentary tickets courtesy of your friend, but your friend can easily arrange such tickets on any night you wish. Many important people, including critics, will be at the opening night. Do you still go to the opening night?

You are able to change your booking for another night. However, there turns out to be just one other night that you can change it to and this is inconvenient for you. It is a night on which you had invited some friends over for dinner. To change the booking, you would have to rearrange the dinner. Do you now go tomorrow as you had originally planned?

NO

| YES   *Question ends* |

Your cough persists to the rearranged booking. You still want to see the play very much and seats are now impossible to get for any other night. Do you now go to the play?

QUESTION 162

You happen to live on the boundary between two different education areas. One has a comprehensive school, the other still maintains the old grammar-school system. Your child is at the age to progress to one or the other. Both schools have identical academic records in terms of pupil achievement, facilities, amenities, etc. You have a free choice as to which school your child goes to. Do you elect to send them to the grammar school?

YES

NO

The schools are the same, except that you are not in the grammar-school area. For your child to go there you would have to move house, a move of nearly fifteen miles. This would mean that you and your partner would have further to travel to work and the other amenities that you normally use. Do you move to enable your child to go to the grammar school?

YES | NO   *Question ends* |

You come into some money. You could now afford to send your child to a public school. However, the grammar school has an exemplary academic record. It is on a par with the most successful of the public schools. Do you still choose to send your child to the grammar school?

The academic records are still identical, but the grammar school is in a more affluent area and consequently has better facilities and amenities. Do you now elect to send your child to the grammar school?

NO | YES   *Question ends* |

You come into some money. You could now easily afford to send your child to a public school. Your local comprehensive has a very good academic record, on a par with all but the most successful public schools. Do you now choose to send your child to a public school?

QUESTION 163

You are playing this game with the other people here at the moment, just as you are now. You are asked a question. The problem concerns sex. You realize that if you were to answer honestly as to how you would react to the problem, it would reveal your own true attitudes towards sex to the others. Could there be such a question that would thus cause you to answer dishonestly?

YES

You are playing the game while on holiday with a group of strangers whom you have been with for a few weeks in the hotel. It is the last night and you know that you will never see any of them again. You are asked that particular question. Would you still answer dishonestly?

YES

NO   *Question ends*

You are playing with a group consisting of your closest friends. You are asked that question again. Do you still answer dishonestly?

NO

You are playing the game with a group of workmates none of whom you would categorize as close friends and one or two of whom you actually dislike. Could there now be such a question that would cause you to answer dishonestly?

NO

YES   *Question ends*

You are playing the game with a group who are all members of your immediate family. Could there now be such a question that would cause you to answer dishonestly?

QUESTION 164

You are queuing for a bus. You are not in any particular hurry. There are many other people in the queue. When the bus comes, it is almost full. As you reach the bus, the conductor says that there is room for one more only. You are directly in front of the platform. However, in all the jostling you have got there before the person who had been in front of you in the queue, a middle-aged man. He is perfectly ordinary. The empty seat is upstairs. Do you board the bus quickly and nip upstairs rather than let the man take the last place?

YES — — — — — — — — — — — **NO** — — — — — — — —

As you leap on to the bus, the man shouts out that he was next. The conductor happens to be in your way. The man takes the opportunity to step on to the platform as well. The conductor says that the bus will not leave until one of you gets off. The man claims that you queue-jumped, the conductor is inclined to take your side as you were on the bus first. Nobody else in the queue says anything. The conductor asks the man to get off. The man begins to do so complainingly. Do you keep silent and permit the man to be turned off the bus?

YES | NO   *Question ends* |

In this instance, the only place on the bus is downstairs. The person who was in front of you was an old lady with some awkward bags of shopping. She says nothing, either because she is unaware that you were behind her or is too shy. Do you allow her to take her rightful place on the bus?

In this instance, you have already had to wait quite a while. There is no other bus in sight and this route is notoriously ill-served. You are, again, in no particular hurry. Do you now hop quickly on the bus in place of the man?

NO | **YES**   *Question ends* |

In this instance, when the bus arrived several people ran along the pavement and hopped on it at the head of the queue. They are all now firmly ensconced on the bus. Having been queue-jumped yourself, would you now take the last place rather than let the man get on?

QUESTION 165

You have been to see a film at a cinema during a festival in this country. At the end of the film, the National Anthem is played. The cinema is still mostly full. Some people stand up for the anthem and some remain seated. It is about fifty-fifty. You happen to be seated as it starts. Do you stand up for the National Anthem (and not just to leave!)?

 YES

 NO

You are abroad on holiday. You happen to attend a minor sports meeting in which there are some British competitors. Because of this, the British National Anthem is played. Since the crowd is a mix of many European nationalities, hardly anyone stands. You can see one or two other British holidaymakers standing. You are seated when it starts. Do you stand for the National Anthem?

 YES | **NO**   *Question ends* |

On another occasion, you visit some friends in Northern Ireland. While there, you attend a children's concert at their child's school. Your friends are Catholic as is the school. Though not militant, your friends express some grievance that at Catholic schools the British National Anthem is played at every assembly and the children made to stand. Since this is not done at Protestant schools, they feel it is done for political motives to 'remind' the Catholics that Northern Ireland is part of the United Kingdom. At the end of the school concert, the British National Anthem is played. The children stand under the guidance of their teachers. However, none of the crowd of parents, among whom you are seated, stand. Do you stand for the National Anthem?

On another occasion, you are at a classical concert. At the close, the National Anthem is played. Almost everybody rises to their feet. However, you can see one or two who remain seated. You are seated when it starts. Do you stand for the National Anthem?

NO | **YES**   *Question ends* |

At another time, you visit some friends in Northern Ireland and while there you attend a function with them. Your friends are Protestant, though not militant. However, they point out to you that the Protestants are, in general, proudly loyal to the United Kingdom. The function you attend is a Protestant one. The National Anthem is struck up. Everybody, but everybody, stands up. You are seated as it starts. Do you stand for the National Anthem?

QUESTION 166

Your electricity bill arrives. When you look, you find that it is a receipt. Somehow, the Electricity Board has marked it as paid when you haven't yet paid it. You have been living in the house for some time and this is the first time that this has occurred. Do you notify the Electricity Board that you have not paid the bill?

YES

When you phone the Electricity Board, you are transferred all around the houses until you eventually get someone who is supposed to be in the appropriate department. They check and tell you that as far as their accounts are concerned, your bill has been paid. They suggest that if you are concerned, you can also send payment for the amount which will be held as credit against your next payment should there prove to be no error on this current bill, which they will now recheck more thoroughly. Do you send them the payment?

YES   NO   *Question ends*

When your next bill is due, you again receive a receipt showing that your bill has been paid. It also shows that you still have credit to the amount that you previously sent in. Something is still wrong. Your bills are mysteriously being paid. Do you notify the Electricity Board again to try to sort it out?

NO

In this instance, you have only recently moved into your home. This would have been your first bill. It could be that the previous occupant has inadvertently paid it by means of a standing order. You do not know, nor have you met the previous occupant. Do you now notify the Electricity Board about the error?

NO   YES   *Question ends*

You learn from a neighbour that the previous occupant was an elderly man. He had health problems and his family decided that he would be better off in a home for the elderly, which was why he moved out. The old man was senile and had difficulty remembering things. Consequently, he paid most of his bills in instalments by standing orders. You realize that he has probably inadvertently paid your bill. Do you now try to sort out the error?

QUESTION 167

Someone has made an offer for your house of the asking price, which you have accepted. The house is taken off the market. Before the deal is finalized, however, you receive a call from a man who looked round the house a month ago but made no offer. He says that something fell through for·him and he is now desperate to move. He offers £3,000 more. The woman whose offer you had accepted was a friendly woman with whom you had got on well. She cannot afford to offer more. You barely remember the man, and even then only as quiet and reticent. Do you accept his late offer and let the woman down?

YES

NO

The woman is very upset and writes a note to say that she feels that you have acted dishonourably. Simultaneously, the man withdraws the higher offer. Do you tell the woman that you have reconsidered and feel honour bound to offer her the house, rather than admit the truth or omit to contact her?

Three months pass before you find a house that you would like. It is £4,000 over the maximum price you can afford, however. In the meantime you have kept your prospective buyer waiting three months. She has spoken to you regularly on friendly and amicable terms. The man gets in touch with you again and renews his bid of £3,000 over the asking price. Do you now accept the higher offer?

YES | NO   *Question ends* |

The woman accepts your explanation and negotiations recommence. However, the man contacts you again. He is more desperate than ever as another deal has fallen through. He offers to pay the extra £3,000 in cash immediately. Do you now go back on your word of 'honour' to the woman and accept the man's offer?

NO | YES   *Question ends* |

The same situation, except that the woman has been rather a nuisance over the three months, constantly chivvying you and moaning about the delay. The man, on the other hand, has been friendly and reasonable. Do you now accept his higher offer?

QUESTION 168

You have been shipwrecked with a group of people none of whom you knew previously. You have been without food for so long that one of your number has died. Would you eat that person if this were the only way to stay alive?

 YES

 NO

You have been shipwrecked with the people playing this game. Once again, one of them dies. Would you eat them if this were the only way to stay alive?

 YES

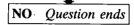 NO· *Question ends*

If the partner of the person who died were there and still alive and they begged you not to eat their dead partner, would you still do so?

All the others do so. Time passes and another person dies. You are so weak, that you know that if you do not eat them, you will be the next to die and to be cannibalized. Would you now eat the person who has just died?

 NO

YES *Question ends*

You are now very weak. You have not long to go. There is a beach nearby where things drift out to sea because of the currents. Do you choose to die on the island and be cannibalized rather than throw yourself into the sea?

QUESTION 169

The seventeen-year-old son of your best friends comes to see you. He tells you that he is in need of advice and for reasons that become obvious he cannot talk to his parents. He is having an affair with the wife of a colleague of his father. You know the woman, though not well. He has fallen under her spell; she is about ten years older than he is, and he is totally besotted with her. He knows that his father would go berserk if he were to find out and could well kick him out of the house. He wishes the relationship to remain secret and knows there will be problems all round if it were to come out in the open, as he suspects it will one day. He has been in a quandary and needs to speak to someone in confidence, just to get it off his chest. Regardless of what advice you give him, he will continue the relationship and not tell his parents. Do you tell his parents?

 YES -

 NO

Before you do, the father comes to visit you. He says his son has become moody lately and that he has seen him out with this woman. He tells you that he suspects his son is having an affair with her and adds that if he is, he'll knock some sense into the blighter and kick him out on his ear. Do you now go ahead and tell the parents?

 YES

| **NO** *Question ends* |

In this instance, you know that the boy's mother is just recovering from a nervous breakdown. She is almost back to normal but any distress at this time should be avoided. When the father comes to you, do you still tell him?

The boy comes to you again and tells you that he is planning to run off with the woman. He asks you to explain to his parents after the deed is done so that they will not worry about his safety. They plan to go in a month or so's time. Do you tell the parents beforehand?

 NO

| **YES** *Question ends* |

In this instance, you happen to know the woman concerned quite well. She has had several affairs before. If she is running true to form, she is using the young boy to get at her husband. The longer it continues, the more pain there will be all around. Do you now tell the parents?

QUESTION 170

You have just made a very good deal on a one-year-old house near your new place of work. The house is immaculate and you feel that you have a bargain. As you are moving in, one of your new neighbours comes over to welcome you. He respectfully enquires how much you paid for your property as he is trying to sell his and was surprised to see your house sold so quickly. You then notice that several other For Sale signs have gone up along the street. It is a very cold January day, so you invite him in to ask about the reasons for all the sudden selling activity. He is surprised that you ask and explains that since you bought this house, some of the others thought that they'd try their luck at selling theirs. The reason, he explains, is that — the houses are not far from a sewage farm. Every summer, but only in the hot weather, the wind brings the most disgustingly foul smells wafting into the homes. Everybody moved in the previous February. Come summer, they discovered why the houses had been so cheap. Your vendor did not tell you this even though you had specifically asked about local factors: was there any traffic noise, a lot of children or *anything* else you should know about? The vendor said that there was nothing. Consequently, you have paid well over the true value of the house. Do you try to take the vendor to court to make them buy back the house?

YES

NO

Your solicitor tells you that it would be an interesting case as to whether you could prosecute and feels that it may set a precedent. They agree that you have been ripped off but estimate your chances of winning as fifty-fifty. They also estimate that it would cost you a minimum of £5,000 should you not be awarded costs. Do you still go to court?

June comes, and with it the first heatwave. You have not been able to sell the house. The smell from the sewage farm is disgusting. Do you now try to go to court?

NO

| **YES** *Question ends* |

The local council buys up three of the houses along the road to house the homeless. They have paid about one-third of the price you paid. Do you now try to go to court?

YES

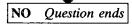
| **NO** *Question ends* |

A little later, your solicitor advises you that the costs could well be higher as you will need specialist advice. He estimates this to cost £7,500 extra and advises you not to continue as your chances are still the same. The decision, however, is yours. Do you still go to court?

QUESTION 171

You are strolling along the street. As you pass a smart restaurant, you notice an unmarked envelope on the pavement that seems to contain something. You pick it up and peek inside to find two tickets for specified seats at an event that you have always wanted to go to – the Wimbledon finals, for example. Such tickets are normally far beyond your means. From the condition of the envelope, it has not been on the pavement long and its position would indicate that it was dropped by somebody entering or leaving the restaurant. Do you inquire at the restaurant to try to find the owner rather than keep the tickets for your own purposes?

 YES

 NO

As you push back the flap, you spot another piece of paper that had been concealed. This turns out to be a complimentary ticket for a free champagne lunch at the event. There is no name or identification on it. Do you still try to find the owner rather than keep the tickets for your own purposes?

 YES　　　| **NO**　*Question ends* |

In this instance, there is no free champagne lunch and the tickets are not for specific seats. They are such that nobody would be able to identify you as an interloper on somebody else's tickets. Do you still try to find the owner?

As you are strolling off, you glance back at the noise of the restaurant door opening. You see a well-heeled gentleman come out. He is patting his pockets and looking at the pavement rather disconcertedly. Do you go back to check if he is looking for the tickets?

 NO　　　| **YES**　*Question ends* |

If you had intended to sell the tickets, you are unable to do so. Shortly before the event, you notice an ad in your paper. It is offering a reward of £150 for the return of two tickets for the event that were lost outside the restaurant where you found them. The phone number of the owner is given. Do you now try to return the tickets to the owner?

198

QUESTION 172

You are in a small shop near your home although it is not one you visit regularly.
While in there, you see an old lady take a small packet of sweets from a shelf and
slip it into her handbag. She then makes for the door to leave. You are at the counter
being served and are the only one to have noticed this. Do you do anything about
it?

 YES

 NO

You are in a large supermarket rather
than a small shop. Would you now do
anything?

As the old lady slips the sweets into her
bag, you notice several other obviously
newly taken items in there which she
covers up with a scarf. This is more than
a whim. Do you now do anything?

 YES | NO   *Question ends* |

The old lady lives near you and you know
of her. She is quite house-proud and
inoffensive. Whenever you have passed
her in the street, she has always smiled
sweetly and said hallo. Would you now
do anything?

NO | YES   *Question ends* |

You leave the shop. Outside there is a
bus stop with a few people waiting. The
old lady is at the back of the queue and
you are a little behind her. She is
unaware of your presence since, to your
surprise, you see her taking the purse
from the open bag of the old lady in front
of her in the queue. After pocketing it,
she starts to toddle off down the road
away from you. Do you now do anything?

QUESTION 173

You are stony broke and desperate for some cash to pay some bills. You mention this to a friend in a pub. An acquaintance of theirs whom you have never met is there. This person asks you if you are really broke and you assure them that you are. Your friend pops off to the toilet. While they are gone, their acquaintance tells you that they have a job you can do which will earn you a lot of money very fast – £1,000 in fact. All you must do is take a briefcase from this country to another European city. However, he tells you that if you ask no questions you'll be told no lies. He will say nothing further. Do you accept this job?

 YES

 NO

You meet with this person again in private to be given the details. The money will be transferred into your account on delivery of the briefcase. You will be able to check on this. You must pick up the briefcase from an address in London and then fly from Heathrow to Athens. There, someone will meet you off the plane. Do you still accept the job?

 YES | NO   *Question ends* |

You are given your plane ticket. When you look, you find that you are booked on an Israeli airline. Do you still accept the job?

This brings the immediate response of, 'Well, OK, I'll make it £5,000 and that's as much as the job's worth.' Do you now accept the job?

 NO | YES   *Question ends* |

They then tell you that all the job involves is picking up a briefcase in London and taking the overnight train ferry to Amsterdam where you drop off the briefcase. Do you now accept?

QUESTION 174

It is just after lunchtime and you are beavering away at your place of work. Suddenly, the peace is shattered by some incredibly loud punk music. Loud enough to make the walls vibrate. On investigating, you find that a punk club is opening just down the street and that a one-off celebratory party is being held on the roof with a live band. You can see many brightly coloured punks dancing and enjoying themselves on the rooftop. Other than the loudness of the music, there is nothing really to complain about. It looks as though the party will be going on for the rest of the day. Someone pops in from the adjacent office to collect names for a complaint to the police about the noise. Do you agree with this complaint?

YES

The police arrive in excessive force, considering it is only a complaint about the noise. There are three van-loads, four police-cars, two motorcycles, and several on foot with walkie-talkies running from nearby streets. This cavalcade attracts you and other staff to the street where a sizeable crowd of onlookers has gathered. Beside you in the crowd is a group of Rastafarians who have come out of the reggae-music shop next door to see what is going on. Without warning or provocation, one of the policemen on foot wades into the Rastafarians, pushing one to the ground. Other policemen immediately join in. No violence or provocation is offered at any stage by the Rastafarians, other than spoken objections to their treatment. You see and hear the entire incident at close hand. It is entirely unjustified and unjustifiable. The policemen drag some of the Rastafarians off to a van. Shortly after, the Rastafarian owner of the music shop approaches you with an impromptu petition complaining about the police behaviour towards his customers just now. Do you agree with this complaint?

YES ◀

Later that afternoon, a worker from down the street comes round with another petition. This is to complain to the council about the punk club. They feel that it should not be allowed in the area. The area is mostly business; however, apart from this opening party, the club is in a sound-proofed basement and will only be open in the evenings when all the businesses are closed. Do you agree with this complaint?

| **NO** | *Question ends* |

NO

Somebody rings the police who arrive in excessive force considering it is only a complaint about the noise. There are three van-loads, four police-cars, two motorcycles, and several on foot with walkie-talkies running from nearby streets. This cavalcade attracts you and other staff to the street where a sizeable crowd of onlookers has gathered. Beside you in the crowd is a group of Rastafarians who have come out of the reggae-music shop next door to see what is going on. Without warning or provocation, one of the policemen on foot wades into the Rastafarians, pushing one to the ground. Other policemen immediately join in. No violence or provocation is offered at any stage by the Rastafarians, other than spoken objections to their treatment. You see and hear the entire incident at close hand. It is entirely unjustified and unjustifiable. The policemen drag some of the Rastafarians off to a van. Shortly after, the Rastafarian owner of the music shop approaches you with an impromptu petition complaining about the police behaviour towards his customers just now. Do you agree with this complaint?

YES *Question ends*

► **NO**

Shortly after, a worker from down the street comes round with another petition. This is to complain to the council about the punk club. They feel that it should not be allowed in the area. The area is mostly business. However, apart from this opening party, the club is in a sound-proofed basement and will only be open in the evenings when all the businesses are closed. Do you agree with this complaint?

QUESTION 175

You head off to a hotel in the Lowlands of Scotland for a four-day break. It is a rainy, windswept night as you pull up outside the hotel – an old laird's house perched on the moors. You can see no lights. You enter to find the place dimly lit by candles. The owner apologizes for this and explains that there has been a power cut which should be righted by morning. You are shown to your room. It is very large with oak-panelled walls. The room is dominated by a beautifully carved four-poster bed. By candlelight, it looks very atmospheric and romantic.

After a cosy candlelit dinner and a few drams beside the roaring log fire downstairs, the owner gives you some candles to help you find your way back to the room. He has obviously had a few drams himself as his tongue has been loosened. He tells you about your room. Although it is the best in the hotel, he usually has trouble letting it because of stories of ghostly hauntings. It was the laird's bedroom over a hundred years ago. Then one dark, stormy night, much like tonight, he, his wife and their child were stabbed to death in the very bed still in the room. Now, it is said that the laird returns, crashing around the room in anguish and grief, while his tormented wife is seen wailing in the corridors as she searches for her dead child. At this point, the owner's wife joins you and chides her husband for telling you such tall stories just as you are about to go to bed. They are about to retire, as were you. However, do you now ask for a different room?

 YES

 NO

The wife tells her husband off rather severely. She explains that he loves telling people this story, but in fact they have run the place for twenty years and nobody has ever seen any ghost in all that time. Do you still insist on a different room?

You go to bed. Around midnight the banging starts. It is quiet at first, but loud clatterings occur at intermittent intervals. It sounds like a shutter banging in the wind, but it is unnerving. In between, you can hear the owner and his wife still downstairs. Do you go and ask for a different room?

YES

 | NO . *Question ends* |

It turns out that all the rooms are full. The only thing available is an entire suite. This will cost you an extra £110 plus V A T, which is just about the limit of your finances. Do you take this rather than stay in the laird's old room?

NO

 | YES *Question ends* |

The banging continues. Then a low moaning starts. It sounds like the wind. However, the drams have their effect and you must go to the toilet. While there, you notice that the banging and moaning is not so noticeable as in your room. As you come out, you bump into . . . the owner and his wife going to bed. Do you now ask for a different room?

QUESTION 176

A close friend is organizing a local summer fête. They ask you to go along dressed as a clown to provide some colour and atmosphere. However, you will have to provide your own costume. You have nothing else arranged on the day in question. There will be other people there in various costumes. Do you agree to go as a clown?

YES

Your friend comes to you again. Someone else has backed out and they are turning to you at short notice. You must still go as a clown but you will also be required to stand in a pillory and have wet sponges thrown at you by the local children. Do you agree to go and do this?

YES | NO   *Question ends*

The same request as previously, except you know the fête to be in an area where the children are rather rough, tough and boisterous. Do you still agree to stand in the pillory and have wet sponges thrown at you?

NO

You hear that several of your other friends have volunteered and will all be going in costume. The organizer contacts you again and says that they would be able to provide you with a clown outfit. Do you now agree to go as a clown?

NO | YES   *Question ends*

You hear through your friends already going that a big fancy-dress party has been arranged after the fête at a local big-wig's large and spacious house. All costumed helpers at the fête are invited as a reward for giving their time. Most of your friends will be going to the fête and on to the party. The organizer phones you again to ask if you'll go as a clown. Do you now agree to do it?

QUESTION 177

You and a friend are baby-sitting for some close friends. You decide to have a game of Scrabble. Your friends have a fifteen-year-old son who is away at the moment. While rummaging in his room for the Scrabble set you find soft-core pornographic magazines of the *Penthouse* variety hidden away. Do you inform his parents?

 YES   **NO**

The same situation, except that your friends' son is nineteen. Do you still tell his parents?

 YES | **NO**   *Question ends* |

The same situation, except that you do not know the people for whom you are baby-sitting. You have stepped in to replace a friend who could not make it at the last minute. Do you still tell the parents?

The same situation, except that the magazines you find are hard-core porn but involve only 'normal' sex. Do you now tell the parents?

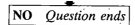 **NO** | **YES**   *Question ends* |

 NO

The same situation, except that you find several magazines. All involve various highly abnormal sexual practices varying from sadism to bestiality. Do you now tell the parents?

QUESTION 178

You are in a large department store when you notice a shoplifter at work. They have pocketed an expensive item of jewellery. You know that the item will not activate the alarm system at the door. If you say nothing, the thief will get away scot free. Do you tell the shop assistant?

YES

NO

Before you can say anything, you half recognize the shoplifter. It is the friend of a friend of yours. You have only met this person once or twice but you know through your friend that they have been having a very bad time recently and have had emotional problems. Do you still tell the shop assistant?

The situation is the same, except that the shop assistant is a friend of yours. Do you tell the shop assistant, your friend, about the shoplifter?

NO

| **YES**   *Question ends* |

YES

| NO   *Question ends* |

The situation is the same, except that you immediately recognize the shoplifter. It is a very close friend of yours, someone you know to be in severe financial difficulties. They have not seen you, being too intent on their shoplifting. Do you tell the shop assistant?

You know the policy of the store is to dock shop assistant's wages if anything is shoplifted from their section. This is to keep the staff vigilant as the store has had severe problems with theft. Your friend is the assistant for the jewellery section that the shoplifter stole the item from. Do you tell your friend, the shop assistant, about the shoplifter?

206

QUESTION 179

Your country is at war. Your country had no alternative as war was declared and commenced by an aggressor. The battlefields are, at the moment, overseas, but there is a real possibility that your country could be invaded if things were to go badly. There is talk that conscription may be introduced. At the moment, if you enlist voluntarily, you can choose your branch of the army, navy or air force. Do you enlist?

 YES

 NO

The situation is the same, except that your country is the aggressor for reasons that you disagree with and feel unjustifiable. However, there is still a danger that should things go badly, your country could be invaded. Do you still enlist?

 YES   NO   *Question ends*

The war is entirely overseas. There is no danger whatsoever of your country being invaded. You believe your country to be the aggressor and entirely in the wrong. Do you still enlist?

Conscription is introduced. You get your call-up papers. Do you enlist now?

 NO   **YES**   *Question ends*

You now live in another country. This country has never been involved in a war, nor is it remotely possible that it will be. However, it has an army and conscription. You get your call-up for one year's service. Conscientious objectors must spend a year in a closed camp doing community work. Do you now enlist?

QUESTION 180

You are playing Monopoly with some friends. There is a hotel on Mayfair. If you were to land there, you would be out of the game. You throw the dice and move, missing Mayfair by one. However, you realize that you miscounted your move and should have landed on Mayfair. Do you keep quiet about your mistake?

 YES

 NO

You are on holiday and have somehow become involved in a game of cards for money with some strangers. You do not particularly like them and the stakes are small. You find that if you move your chair slightly you can see most of their hands reflected in a nearby mirror. Do you move your chair to see their hands from now on?

YES

| NO   *Question ends* |

The same situation except that you are playing cards with some close friends. The stakes are quite high and you know that some of your friends could not afford to lose much. Would you still move your chair to see their hands in the mirror?

You are playing cards with some close friends for highish stakes. You cannot afford to lose much. You find that if you move your chair slightly, you can see most of their hands reflected in a nearby mirror. Do you move your chair to see their hands from now on?

NO

| YES   *Question ends* |

The same situation, except that you have somehow become entangled in a game for high stakes with strangers none of whom you particularly like. You also suspect that they are teaming up against you in the play. Do you now move your chair to see their hands in the mirror?

QUESTION 181

You are in a hurry. While reversing into a tight parking space, you smash the headlamp and damage the grille of the car behind. The car is a standard middle-range saloon of the kind often used by company representatives. You have never claimed on your insurance and to do so now would lose you your no-claims bonus. Do you leave a note giving your name and address?

YES

NO

The same situation, except that the car you have damaged is a brand-new Rolls-Royce. Do you still leave your name and address?

YES

| **NO**   *Question ends* |

This time the car is an old Morris Minor which was made before number plates had a letter suffix. It already has several other dents, scrapes and patches of rust. Do you still leave your name and address?

The same situation, except the car you have damaged is a seven-year-old family saloon with a kiddy-seat in the back. Do you now leave a note with your name and address?

NO

| **YES**   *Question ends* |

This time the car you have damaged is a special car for a disabled person. Do you now leave your name and address?

QUESTION 182

You are at a sporting event. A youth near you continues to shout abuse and express his views loudly in the most obscene and profane language. He does not seem particularly large or otherwise aggressive. Do you ask him to stop swearing?

 YES

 NO

The youth agrees, but is subsequently joined by four of his friends. They all proceed then to swear loudly as before. The friends look more like hooligans. You are on your own. Do you ask them to stop swearing?

The situation is the same, except that you have a young child with you. Do you ask the youth to stop swearing?

 YES

| NO   *Question ends* |

NO

| **YES**   *Question ends* |

They tell you to mind-your-own-business-or-else very aggressively. You are joined at this point by a girlfriend. She is offended by their foul language and asks you to ask them to stop. Do you ask them to stop swearing?

The situation is as before, except that this time you have a girlfriend with you. She is offended by the youth's language and asks you to tell him to stop. Do you ask the youth to stop swearing?

QUESTION 183

While you are at work one day, you come across evidence to prove that the company by which you are employed is doing something illegal. No further information can be had as you are told simply that it is not your department and does not concern you. The company has always treated you fairly and it would be difficult for you to find another job as well paid and interesting. The illegality is simply concerned with avoidance of certain import and export duties though it does involve several hundreds of thousands of pounds. Do you notify the authorities, either anonymously or otherwise?

YES

Before you can notify the authorities, further information comes your way. From this you can see that if the authorities were to take action and the company forced to continue this aspect of its business legally, it would result in the closure of a small subsidiary which employs about twenty people who would lose their jobs. Your job would not be at risk. Do you still notify the authorities?

 YES | NO *Question ends* |

The same situation as so far, except that the illegality is concerned with the avoidance of payment of tax duties abroad to foreign governments only. The company does not avoid any tax in this country. Do you still notify the authorities?

NO

The same situation, except that the company is breaking the law with regard to building regulations. Certain things are being done to cut costs which, in the long run, will involve others in extremely expensive repairs and remedies. Do you now notify the authorities?

 NO | YES *Question ends* |

You come across further information. Not only is the company breaking building regulation law, but it is involved in skirting round health and safety laws with regard to its own workers on sites and in factories. These practices could have fatal consequences. Do you now notify the authorities?

QUESTION 184 (non-vegetarian)

You and some friends are at an international festival. You all enter the gourmet pavilion where there are rare and exotic foods to be tasted. You are presented with various dishes of mouth-wateringly prepared food, exquisitely served. The organizers have been considerate enough to tell you what the dishes contain in advance. The first dish is spare rib of monkey. Do you eat it?

 YES

NO

The ribs are garnished with something you cannot identify. On checking, you find that the garnish is termites dropped in honey. Do you still eat it?

 YES | NO   *Question ends* |

You take your plate of spare rib of monkey garnished with termites dropped in honey. As you prepare to eat it, something stirs on your plate. They forgot to tell you about the trimmings: live Lusitanian snails fed on ginger and sorrel leaves. Do you eat these as well?

All the friends whom you've gone with are eating and obviously enjoying the dish. They explain that it tastes like a cross between beef and pork and is very tasty. Do you now eat some?

 NO | YES   *Question ends* |

In this instance, there is also a delicious sauce surrounding the meat that is made from a fruit base. Do you try some of the sauce with a little rice or bread?

QUESTION 185

You had forgotten that your passport had expired and you are now having to get it renewed in double-quick time for your holiday. You have to report to some offices to clear up some points on the forms. You are shown in to a very busy office and to one desk in particular. To your surprise it is somebody you recognize: the school bully who once made your young life miserable. They look up and recognize you. One quick reference to the snivelling worm you once were and one spittle-splashed bray of that fat face are all you need to remind you that here is someone you hate. While they are rummaging on their desk for your forms, the fat brute disturbs some official-looking papers at the end of the desk. They slide off gracefully into the wastepaper bin unnoticed except by you. You can see that they are not your forms. Do you tell them about the papers that have fallen into the bin?

 YES   **NO**

Before you can say anything, your old bully's superior comes over in a raging temper. Your 'chum' is in hot water for losing some important documents. They are warned that if it happens again, they'll be out on their ear. The superior then strides off. Do you now say anything about the documents that have just fallen into the bin?	At that moment, your old bully's obvious superior comes over in a raging temper. Your 'chum' is apparently in hot water for losing some important documents. They are warned that if it happens again, they'll be out on their ear. The superior then strides off. Do you now say anything about the documents that have just fallen in the bin?

 YES | **NO** *Question ends* | **NO** | **YES** *Question ends* |

As you lean forward and open your mouth, they turn to you and tell you to shut up. A quick run-through of all the names they used to call you tells you that they are still as much of a bully as they ever were. Do you still try to say anything about the documents that have fallen into the bin?	While you wait for your forms to be sorted out, you glance down the office. The cleaning lady is coming. She is emptying the bins into a large sack. The documents are lying clearly in the top of the bin. She will cerainly spot that they should not be there and put them back on the desk. However, you have the remains of your lunch and a newspaper in your bag. If you dump these in the bin, the documents will soon disappear for good and your old enemy will be in trouble. Do you, however, refrain from covering the documents with your rubbish?

QUESTION 186 (female)

You are single. As the result of an indiscretion, you find that you are pregnant. Apart from rape, are there any circumstances in which you would have an abortion?

YES

NO

You are not in love with the father and have in fact gone your separate ways. For you to have a child now would be inconvenient as you would not be able to continue your work and it would push you to the limit financially. You know the father is hard up too and, although willing, would not be able to contribute much. Would this be enough to persuade you to have an abortion?

 YES

| NO   Question ends |

Having the child would not cause any difficulties in your finance or work. However, it would cause problems with your life as a single person. Would this be enough to persuade you to have an abortion?

During tests at the hospital, you are told that the child is suffering from Down's Syndrome. Would you now consider having an abortion?

 NO

| **YES**   *Question ends* |

If the child had been the result of a rape by a stranger without other physical violence, would you then consider having an abortion?

QUESTION 187

As you pass a neighbour's house, you notice a £10 note lying on their footpath. They have a front garden and the note is inside their gate. You are on amicable terms with your neighbours, though they are not close friends. You are not broke. Do you go and hand it in to them?

YES

NO

You are at home when a neighbour's child knocks on your door. They have found a £10 note on your pathway. You don't recall being £10 short nor, when you check, do you seem to have lost one. It was not there when you came home a while ago and nobody has entered or left the house since. Do you let the child keep the money?

YES

NO   *Question ends*

The child is at your door again, except that this time there has been a recent visitor. Another neighbour, with whom you do not have a particularly good relationship, called to complain about the level at which you play your music. The note was probably dropped by him. Do you tell the child to return the note to this man?

You are going to a friend's house for dinner. You are their only guest. You open their front gate and start up the path. As you near their front door, you find a £10 note on their footpath. Do you hand it in to your friend?

NO

YES   *Question ends*

After dinner, as you are reclining on the sofa, your keys slip down the lining of the seat. While retrieving them you find a £10 note. Your friend is in the kitchen at the moment making some coffee. Do you tell them about the £10 note?

QUESTION 188

You are staying with some friends. One evening, they go to the cinema. You've already seen the film so you volunteer to stay in and baby-sit. The youngest have all gone to bed. You are lounging in front of the television with your friends' fourteen-year-old daughter. A news item comes on about a famous pop star just convicted of a drug offence. The young girl asks you if you've ever taken any drugs, not of the medicinal kind. You have no idea what her parents' attitude towards drugs is, although they are good friends. Do you answer the daughter's question truthfully?

YES

Your answer seems to amuse her. She giggles. She then proceeds to talk about a boy at her school, and this and that, culminating in whether she is attractive or not. She then asks you if you've ever been sexually attracted to or 'turned on' by anyone under the age of consent. She is not referring to herself. Do you answer this question truthfully?

YES | NO   *Question ends* |

Your answer seems to quieten her. A bit later, something on the television sparks her off again. She tells you about a shop near her school where they have Walkmans and other things that she likes but can't afford. She says that it would be dead easy to steal something from this shop as everything is just sitting around and the assistant is a bit dozy. She then asks you if you've ever stolen anything. Do you answer this question truthfully?

NO

The same situation, except that your friend's daughter is sixteen years old. Would you now answer her question truthfully?

NO | **YES** · *Question ends* |

In this instance, your friends' daughter is a nineteen-year-old just back from her first year away from home at university. Would you now answer her question truthfully?

216

QUESTION 189

You have been doing very well in a new job and you have been invited to the managing director's house for the first time. Others in the company tell you that this can only mean one thing – promotion. Everybody stresses the importance of staying on the right side of the MD. Impress him and you could go far. On the other hand, people have been ousted from the company because of a personal dislike.

It is a very opulent and impressive house. The evening is going very well and you are feeling slightly pleased with yourself when you nip upstairs to use the bathroom. As you pass the main bedroom, the door is open. Through the open door and the far window you can see a magnificent view. You inadvertently take a step forward to see better and unfortunately catch a small table. A small crystal perfume bottle topples, falls on to the marble doorstop, shatters and showers its expensive contents across the carpet.

Do you own up to having broken the bottle in the MD's bedroom?

 YES

 NO

As you come back downstairs, you can hear the managing director's wife talking about the romantic honeymoon present given to her on her wedding night – an antique crystal perfume bottle. It is – was – her most treasured possession. Do you still own up to having broken it?

 YES   **NO   *Question ends***

Before you can do so, the phone rings. The managing director goes to answer it and his wife takes the opportunity to slip into the kitchen. As you wait for them to return, you hear the wife go upstairs. She returns looking upset just as her husband finishes his phone call and returns. Before you can say anything, you hear her tell her husband that the damn' cat must have been in the bedroom again and that it has knocked over and broken the treasured perfume bottle. Do you still own up that it was you who broke the bottle?

The boss goes upstairs as you return. He comes back and tells his wife that he could smell perfume and that a bottle had been broken. The boss concludes that it must have been the cat, which seems to have a habit of breaking things. He comments that anything else will be the last straw and that they'll get shot of the damn' thing. Do you now own up that it was you who broke the bottle?

 NO   **YES   *Question ends***

In this instance, they have no cat. The wife is distraught that the bottle was broken as it was a treasured family antique. She says that it must have been Mrs Kitts, the elderly cleaning lady who, apparently, often breaks things. She says that this is the last straw and that Mrs Kitts will have to be sacked. Do you now own up?

QUESTION 190

There is a general election. The party for whom you voted at the previous election is in disarray. It has been rocked by some personal scandals and torn by internecine strife. All the pundits are agreed that this party has no chance of winning this election. However, the party is still espousing exactly the same policies that caused you to vote for it in the previous election. The other parties are espousing exactly the same policies that decided you against them and still have the same leaders. Do you still vote for the same party, or abstain from voting, rather than vote for one of the other parties? Or if you deliberately abstained before, do you do so again?

 YES

 NO

Just before the election, one of the parties you do not support makes a statement on what you believe to be the most important single issue. They actually proclaim that they will do exactly what you believe should be done, although their other policies remain the same. The party you usually support has never done this, though they have been near this position. Do you still vote as you did last time?

One of the other parties is stating that it plans generous cuts in income tax, especially in the bracket which includes you. Is this enough for you to give it your vote?

 YES | NO · *Question ends* |

NO | YES   *Question ends* |

A party you do not support wins the election. Shortly afterwards . . . catastrophe! The prime minister and many of the new cabinet are assassinated in a terrorist bomb attack. Parliament decides to hold another general election immediately, on principle, to show that the people cannot be intimidated by terrorism. Do you still vote as you did before, rather than for the party that had just won the previous election?

Only one of the other parties has a real chance of preventing the party you most dislike from getting into power. Is this enough for you to give it your vote?

QUESTION 191

You are at home in your house in the country when there is a knock at the door. You open it to see a young couple. They are collecting signatures for a petition opposing the proposed building of an American air base at a site some forty miles away. Little is known of what the base would entail as it is merely a proposal at this time. Do you sign the petition?

 YES   **NO**

A demonstration has been organized at the proposed site. It is due on a day when you habitually do something else, though not of great import – play tennis, swim, shop, etc. Do you go to the demonstration?

 YES | **NO**   *Question ends*

Another demonstration has been organized. At the previous one there was a great deal of violence and many arrests. You know the police will be at this one in great force and that there is likely to be violence. Do you go to the demonstration?

You later discover that if the air base were to be built, the road outside your house would become a main military convoy route. There are plans to widen the road because of this, which show that approximately a quarter of your front garden would be needed. The couple return again with their petition opposing the air base. Do you now sign it?

 NO | **YES**   *Question ends*

Further information on the scheme reveals that an additional supply depot is involved. This would be in the open fields opposite your house. It is also rumoured that the depot would store nuclear weaponry. The couple return with the petition. Do you now sign it?

QUESTION 192

You are travelling back overland from a holiday in Europe. On a train, you meet someone of the opposite sex whom you find attractive and you become travelling companions. You get on very well. They have been holidaying in North Africa. When you arrive back in England, but before you have gone through passport control or customs, they pull you to one side. Your new-found friend explains that they have bought some marijuana back with them. Just a small amount in a matchbox. However, they are now nervous. Their passport shows that they have been to North Africa and they feel that this might cause them to be searched for such drugs. Your passport, however, shows no visit to North Africa, and therefore you are less likely to be searched. They ask you to take the matchbox through for them. You find this person really attractive and would like to continue the relationship once you both get back home since they come from the same place as you. Do you take the matchbox through for them?

 YES   **NO**

In this instance, although you like them very much and have enjoyed their company, you do not want any relationship with them other than just a casual friend. Do you still take the matchbox through for them?

In this instance, your new-found friend is returning home from the Far East. In the matchbox is a small uncut black-market ruby that they picked up cheap in Thailand. Would you take this through for them?

 YES | NO   *Question ends* | **NO** | YES   *Question ends* |

Once again, you would like to continue the relationship as you find them extremely attractive. However, this time they have a largish quantity of the drug, professionally concealed inside something innocent-looking. There is too much just for 'personal use'. They explain that they are short of cash and had hoped to sell it back home to recoup some of the cost of the holiday. Do you take this through customs for them?

In this instance, they have returned from the Far East with an expensive Japanese camera. You have no camera with you and could easily carry it through slung over your shoulder. Since you have not been outside any EEC countries, no one would necessarily suspect its true origins. Do you carry this through for them?

QUESTION 193

You are working in a job in which you have responsibility for commissioning quotes and placing orders with other companies. A company of which you have heard good reports has submitted an extremely competitive quote. It is a toss-up between this company and another. One of their representatives phones you and offers to take you out and treat you to a meal. Do you accept?

 YES

For one reason or another, you do not accept their quote and the work goes to another company. However, they continue to quote and keep in touch. Near Christmas, their representative comes to give you a rather expensive Christmas present. By now, you have become fairly friendly with the representative and the present is something that you like. Do you accept the gift?

 YES | NO *Question ends* |

The representative now intimates that should any work come the way of their company through you, you would get a 5 per cent 'fee'. On the next job that the company quotes for, it is a toss-up between it and the company you normally use. Do you now give the work to the company offering the 5 per cent 'fee'?

 NO

The company has now done several jobs for you and proved extremely good. You are very likely to use it regularly from now on. At Christmas, their representative comes in and gives you a rather expensive present. It happens to be something that you like. Do you accept this gift?

NO | YES *Question ends* |

The company has now built up a very good and long-standing working arrangement with you and your company. You have had a very trying year and feel badly in need of a holiday. You have the time to spare but not the money. The company's representative tells you that there is a company villa and that you would be welcome to use it free of charge. It is in a location that you would like to visit and you would be able to afford all other expenses involved. Do you accept this offer?

QUESTION 194

You have sold some old bric-à-brac at a market and have been paid in cash. On getting home, you notice that one of the £20 notes looks a little odd — a slight difference in colouring, though it could just be old. You cannot find the trader who gave it to you, so you are stuck with it. You are not hard up. Do you try and spend it rather than take it to a bank or the police?

 YES

The first time you try the shopkeeper looks at it closely and then refuses to accept it. He suggests you take it to a bank. Do you still try to spend it elsewhere?

 YES | NO   *Question ends* |

At the next place, the shopkeeper checks the number against a list the police have issued to him. He proclaims it a forgery. You profess total innocence so well that he returns the note to you as you've agreed that you'll take it straight to the police. Do you still continue to try to spend it?

 NO

The situation is the same, except that it is two £50 notes that look a little suspect. You know that if you take them to the police and they prove to be forgeries, the police will keep them. You cannot really afford to lose £100 just like that. Do you now try to spend them?

NO | YES   *Question ends* |

This time, the notes all appear genuine but you are given an Irish 50p piece. Do you try to spend this whether over the counter or in a slot machine?

QUESTION 195

You are in hospital. The friendliest members of staff turn out to be the ward orderlies with whom you frequently have enjoyable chats. However, you are horrified at the state of the shared lavatory and washing facilities. You feel sure that they are a health hazard. Do you speak to the ward sister about this, even though it may get the orderlies into trouble?

YES   **NO**

Before you have a chance to do so, you mention this to another patient. They agree with you but have heard that it is the result of a work-to-rule by the orderlies in protest against government cuts in the health service. Do you still complain to the ward sister?

One morning you go to use the facilities. You have just had a minor operation and have been told to keep very clean. However, everything is dirty, there is no toilet paper and the baths have a thick grimy ring around the inside. Do you now complain to the ward sister?

 YES | **NO** *Question ends*

 NO | **YES** *Question ends*

The ward sister is sympathetic to your complaints. However, she points out that an outside private company now has the contract for cleaning these facilities. Because of its poor standards, the orderlies have been having to do extra work to make good the company's shortcomings. The orderlies are now working to rule in protest at this and the dirty conditions. She adds that if you wish to complain, it would be more effective to write to your MP with your complaints. Do you now complain to your MP?

An elderly patient in the bed next to you complains about the conditions in the toilet and washing facilities. They wish to complain but are feeling too weak and ill to do it themselves. You have got on very well with this person. They ask you to complain on their behalf. Do you now complain to the ward sister?

QUESTION 196

You are in a small shop. It is not one you normally frequent and you know none of the staff. You make a purchase and pay with a £5 note. The assistant inadvertently gives you change for a £10 note. Do you say nothing?

YES **NO**

You are in your local corner shop where you regularly pick up some odds and ends. You know the staff quite well and they have often done you favours and have always been very helpful. They give you change for £10 instead of £5. Do you say nothing?	The same thing happens except this time you are in a very large, busy and impersonal department store. This time do you say nothing?

 YES | NO   *Question ends* |

The next time you are in your local corner shop, the assistant says that they think they made a mistake last time you were in the shop and gave you change for £10 instead of £5. Do you deny it?

 NO | YES   *Question ends* |

You are in the department store again, except that you are in a hurry. The assistant has been particularly unhelpful, verging on the offensive. When you come to paying, the unhelpful assistant makes the same mistake. Do you say nothing?

QUESTION 197

Your partner is out of town for the weekend. You go to a party where you meet somebody whom you find attractive and who finds you attractive. You are very much in love with your partner and view your relationship as a lifelong one. You have had no arguments recently and are very happy. Because of this chance encounter at the party, you have the time and opportunity to sleep with somebody else you happen to find attractive. You know it would cause problems between you and your partner if they were to find out. Do you sleep with this other person?

 YES **NO**

You do so and it is very pleasant and enjoyable. You still love your partner and this new person in your life just does not stir the same emotions. However, they contact you again and intimate that they are available for a casual affair whenever you have the time and the inclination. Do you continue the relationship on this basis?

In this instance, your partner has always said that they would never be annoyed should you sleep with someone else as long as it was just once. They even reiterated this as they left for the weekend. Would you now do so?

NO | **YES**   *Question ends* |

You discover that your partner has slept with someone else. Shortly afterwards, you again happen to see the person you met at the party. They are still interested. Your partner is again away for the weekend. Regardless of whether you argued or not, you still love your partner. However, would you now sleep with this other person?

 YES | **NO**   *Question ends* |

Your partner seldom goes away for weekends. To make time for your affair, you would have to lie and concoct stories. Would you do this to continue the relationship with the other person?

QUESTION 198

You are at a friend's house in your friend's son's bedroom where the son is showing you his expensive computer equipment. The son tells you that he has been hacking successfully. He explains that this means breaking through the security code to gain access to outside computer systems. As an example, he fiddles with his computer for a time. Suddenly you can see on the screen that he has gained access to the computer files of the company for which you work. There is nobody else in the room. He tells you he can pull out the staff salaries. This will enable you to see what your colleagues are earning. Do you tell him to access them so that you can see what they earn?

 YES   **NO**

He then accesses a local bank. You happen to have an elderly relative who does not have long to live. You have always been one of their favourites and it has been presumed in the family that they will leave you quite a lot of what they have. However, nobody knows just how much they have but you know it's all kept in a savings account at this bank. The son tells you he can access any savings account. Do you ask him to access your relative's to find out how much is there?

YES | NO   *Question ends* |

He can access the local hospital records. Your current partner was once there before you ever met and has always been coy and secretive as to why. The son tells you he can access medical records. Do you ask him to access your partner's records?

The son tells you he can access local police records. You have an unpleasant neighbour with whom you do not get on very well. You have often suspected that the neighbour has had trouble with the police. Do you ask him to access information on your neighbour's police record?

NO | **YES**   *Question ends* |

It so happens that the friend whose house you are in is a workmate doing much the same job as you. At this point, the son says, in all innocence, 'I don't know why you don't want to look at your firm's pay records. Dad's often looked at yours.' Do you now ask him to access your firm's pay records?

QUESTION 199

There is an epidemic of German measles going round. As far as you know you've never had German measles. Now you develop a rash on your body but don't otherwise feel ill — it is, after all, a pretty mild disease. However, you are fully aware of the disastrous effects it can have on a pregnant woman who contracts it and of the damage it could cause to an unborn child. It is a pleasant day, you feel like taking a stroll in the sunshine. Do you go out into a public place knowing you might have German measles?

 YES **NO**

You urgently need to go to the bank where it is likely there will be a queue. You happen to know that one of the tellers is pregnant. It is the only bank nearby. Do you go?	You need to go to the bank as a matter of urgency. It is a relatively quiet sub-branch that is quite nearby. You think you can avoid direct contact with anybody. Do you pop down to the bank?

 YES | NO   *Question ends* | **NO** | YES   *Question ends* |

Later that day, you had arranged to meet a friend at a café. She is pregnant and you have been unable to contact her. Do you keep the engagement?	Having settled down in your home to sit out your illness, the phone rings. It is your neighbour. Her child, although in no real danger, has cut itself quite badly and needs to be taken to the hospital to have some stitches put in. The neighbour cannot take the child herself and asks you if you could do it as she has been unable to contact anyone else. You are her last resort. However, you have no car and would have to use public transport for the half-hour journey. Do you take the child to the hospital?

QUESTION 200

You are away from home and staying in a hotel. One evening, as you return to the hotel, you find a £10 note caught up in some rumpled carpet behind the entrance doors. The receptionist happens to be looking your way, though not at you. Nobody else is around and you're not short of money. Do you hand the £10 note in?

YES	NO

Before you can pick up the money, the phone rings and the receptionist turns away to answer it. Do you now hand in the money?

As you pass, the receptionist asks if you found anything as they thought they saw you pick something up. They explain that another guest dropped their handbag a short while ago and the contents had scattered everywhere. After a quick and not very thorough search, they had had to go out as they were in a hurry, so there could still be some of their things lying around. You could easily and plausibly say that you were straightening the rumpled carpet. However, do you now hand in the money?

YES | NO *Question ends*

On another occasion, you are going out of the hotel and find a £10 note in the car park. There is nobody else around. Do you hand this money in?

NO | YES *Question ends*

On another occasion, you are just coming into the hotel when you see the guest entering just in front of you drop a £10 note. They are not aware of the fact. They are a few yards in front of you with their back to you. Nobody else is around and the receptionist is looking the other way. Do you tell the person that they have dropped the money?

QUESTION 201

You are at a party at a large country house one summer's evening with several friends. You are having a really enjoyable time, when later, while you are sitting talking to some people at the side of the swimming pool, the couple whose house it is announce that the pool is free for use. They then strip off and start to swim naked. After a few minutes several others have joined in the nude bathing. It is a hot sultry evening. Some of your friends are already in the pool along with others you don't know. Many other strangers are sitting around the poolside, chatting and drinking. Do you join in the nude bathing?

 YES   **NO**

Soon most of the party is now centred in and around the pool. Virtually everybody is naked. Time has passed and more drink has flowed. Several couples in and around the pool are now lying in each other's arms gently kissing and resting. During this time, someone who you find attractive and who seems to find you attractive has been swimming and talking with you. They now suggest you both rest and lie down by the poolside. They would obviously like to join in the general kissing and embracing going on. Do you consent?

 YES | NO *Question ends* |

After a while, several couples around are actually making love. Your new-found partner makes such advances towards you. You find them very attractive. Would you make love with them with the other couples around?

Soon, virtually everybody is in the pool. On speaking to some others who have not joined in the nude bathing, you find them rather uninteresting. Your friends are all in the pool. Everybody seems to be enjoying themselves and nobody seems self-conscious. Beach balls are being thrown about and there is a general air of fun rather than sex. Do you now join in the nude bathing?

NO | **YES** *Question ends* |

Some others leave. You are now the only person around not naked. The couple who live in the house shout that if you're shy, there are some spare costumes in a poolside hut. Do you now, with or without a costume, join in the bathing?

QUESTION 202

One Saturday afternoon, when you are not particularly busy, there is a ring at your front-door bell. You open it and are very surprised to see two Japanese tourists standing there. In the politest way imaginable, they ask if they may come in for tea. They would appear to be a married couple and do not look at all suspicious to you. Although you've never seen them before, you get the impression that they are totally genuine. There are several other people knocking around your house at the moment and the kettle happens to be on. Do you invite them in for a cup of tea?

 YES   **NO**

Just as you are about to answer, the woman produces a bunch of flowers which she presents to you with a smile. You recognize the flowers — they have obviously just been picked from your front garden (or window box). Do you still invite them in for a cup of tea?

The same situation except that by coincidence, a friend of yours had recently asked some Japanese tourists back to their house for a cup of tea. The tourists had been very grateful and presented your friend with a digital watch. Do you now ask the two on your doorstep in for a cup of tea?

 YES   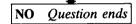 NO   *Question ends*

The same situation except that you are alone at home and the two Japanese tourists are short, thick-set men in smart business suits. Once again, they do not appear suspicious. Do you invite them in for a cup of tea?

 NO   YES   *Question ends*

After hearing your polite refusal, the couple mention your friend's name and say that they were told to call round as you made an excellent cup of English tea. Do you now ask them in?

QUESTION 203

Somehow, regardless of whether you are innocent or not, you have been convicted of a very minor misdemeanour. Your sentence is to perform some community work for a short period, three months, working three evenings a week and alternate weekends. However, you may turn down some of the work offered to you. The first community work extended to you is to help in a home for Down's Syndrome sufferers of all ages. The work would entail helping to supervise their work and play sessions. You do not know what other work options are available. Do you accept this work?

 YES

 NO

Before you can take up the position, it is filled by a full-time worker. You are now offered work in a home for the mentally disturbed. However, none are known to be violent although squabbles between patients have been known. The work would involve simply being available to help the professionals there carry out their duties with the patients. You know nothing of any other options. Do you accept this work?

 YES　　　| NO　Question ends |

The same situation, except that you are offered work with severely physically handicapped people. The work would involve helping to feed, clothe and bathe them, etc. Do you accept this work?

You are next offered work in a home for problem children. You would work closely with individuals under supervision from a professional in the home. Do you accept this work?

NO　　　| YES　Question ends |

You are next offered social work. This would involve calling on old-age pensioners in the area, doing odd jobs and shopping for them and simply checking that they are OK. Do you accept this work?

QUESTION 204

One winter, while you are away from your home, the pipes burst in your loft. All weekend, water pours down inside your house ruining carpets, furniture, books and bringing a ceiling down, too. The mess is appalling. You are totally insured for such damage. However, do you attempt to claim for more than the actual value of replacing and repairing the damage?

 YES

 NO

When you submit your claim, you could over-evaluate to compensate yourself for the inconvenience and to allow for any underpayment by the insurance company. This way, after the claim is settled, you would end up with the actual value of repairing and replacing what was damaged. Do you, however, try to claim more than this in the hope of making a profit at the end of the day?

Before you actually send in your claim, you are discussing the matter with a friend. It happens that they have exactly the same policy with the same company. They also had a similar disaster. Your friend tells you that they sent in a totally honest and accurate claim but the insurance company dickered over the smallest detail so that in the end they only received two-thirds of the amount claimed. Do you now claim for more to compensate for this?

 YES | NO   *Question ends* |

Would you go to the extent of buying some junk from a secondhand shop, damaging it with water and claiming for it, or some other deliberate subterfuge, to be able to claim as much as you possibly could?

 ·**NO** | YES   *Question ends* |

In this instance, at the last renewal of your policy the insurance company had increased your premium by 50 per cent without any explanation. You have had the policy for five years and have never claimed on it. Your friend tells you, as before, what happened when they sent in an accurate claim. Do you now claim for more than the actual value of the damage?

QUESTION 205

You are stony broke and desperate for cash to pay some bills. You mention this to a friend in a pub. An acquaintance of theirs whom you have never met before is also there. This person asks you if you are really broke and you assure them that you are. Your friend pops off to the toilet. While they are gone, their acquaintance tells you that they have a job you can do which will earn you a lot of money very fast – £1,000, in fact. All you must do is pick up a parcel at one point in this country and hand-deliver it to another place in this country. However, he tells you that if you ask no questions, you'll be told no lies. He will say nothing further. Do you accept this job?

 YES

You meet with this person again in private to be given the details. You will be paid on delivery in cash. You must pick up a parcel from an address in London and then fly on the shuttle to Scotland. There, someone will meet you off the plane, give you your money and you will give them the parcel. Do you still accept the job?

 YES | NO   *Question ends*

In this instance, the job is the same except that your destination from London is Belfast. Do you still accept the job?

 NO

This only brings the immediate response of, 'Well, OK. I'll make it £3,000 and that's as much as the job's worth.' Do you now accept the job?

 NO | **YES**   *Question ends*

They then say, 'Look! All you'll have to do is simply pick up a parcel from a left-luggage locker at Euston. Take it with you on the train to Birmingham, then leave it in a left-luggage locker there and bring the key back to me. Then you'll get your cash.' Do you now agree to do the job?

QUESTION 206

You are at a party when a friend introduces you to an astrologer with warm recommendations. For some reason, the astrologer is interested in you, for shortly afterwards you receive in the post a chart they have prepared for you. In an accompanying letter, they say that they hope you don't object and that the friend who introduced you gave them the necessary information. However, in the chart they advise you not to drive on a particular day. You had intended to drive that day but refraining from doing so will neither inconvenience nor be a burden to you. Do you choose to drive on the day in question?

 YES

 NO

Before the day arrives, you are talking on the phone to the friend who introduced you to the astrologer. One of the journeys you had in mind for that particular day involved picking up this friend while you were *en route*. However, they adamantly refuse to drive with you on that day. Do you still choose to drive on the day in question?

The astrologer has given you no reason not to drive. On the day in question it turns out to be a clear sunny day. You had intended visiting a friend you haven't seen in ages and whom you very much want to see. The journey is only an hour's drive. Do you now decide to drive?

 YES | NO   *Question ends* |

 NO | YES   *Question ends* |

On the day in question, you are up and having breakfast. The radio is on. You hear reports of very bad local road conditions with fog and ice, although these are not so bad as to deter you normally. Do you still choose to drive on the day?

It's still the morning of the day in question. You're just having a cup of tea when the phone rings. It is the friend who introduced you to the astrologer. During the conversation it transpires that they actually gave the astrologer some wrong information about the time of your birth. Although the date and year were correct, they inadvertently confused a.m. with p.m. so that the time given for your birth was twelve hours out. The chart is inaccurate. Do you now drive on the day in question?

QUESTION 207

You are at a friend's house and you need to make a telephone call. When you pick up the phone, there is a crossed line or a party line, because you can hear two people talking, a man and a woman. You just catch a few words of an ordinary conversation about what the weather might be like at the weekend for the barbecue, etc. They seem oblivious to the fact that you have linked in to their conversation. Do you continue to listen in?

YES

NO

The woman continues but the man tells her to hold it a minute. He says that he thought he heard a click and thinks somebody has come in on a crossed line. They both go silent, evidently waiting to hear if someone, namely you, hangs up their phone. Do you quietly hold on to listen to their conversation when they resume?

You are just about to hang up quietly when the conversation takes a sudden shift. The couple suddenly refer to events between them last night. The conversation sounds racy, to say the least, from the oddments you catch as you are lowering the phone. Do you now listen in to their conversation?

YES

| NO   *Question ends* |

NO

| YES   *Question ends* |

After a short wait, they decide that there is no crossed line and resume their conversation. Just then your friend in the house calls you. The pair on the phone evidently hear it too for the woman says, 'There is someone listening.' She then asks whoever it is to hang up this instant. Do you stay mum and persist in trying to listen to their conversation?

Suddenly, a name is mentioned. It is that of the friend in whose house you are. Do you now listen in to hear what is being said?

QUESTION 208

You are out on a ramble in the country. As you stroll down a semi-overgrown path, you pass an orchard. The trees are laden with apples, or some other fruit that you sometimes eat. You are not hungry at the moment having just had a meal in a country pub. However, you have a bag with you . The fence around the orchard has tumbled down and it is child's play to step over it. Do you scrump some fruit?

YES   **NO**

In this instance, the fence around the orchard is solid and of barbed wire. It is climbable, but difficult. Also there is a large sign warning that there are guard dogs roaming the orchard. However, you can see neither hide nor hair of any dog. There is nobody else around. Do you still scrump some fruit?

YES | NO   *Question ends* |

You fill your bag and stroll on your way. A little later you pass the rear of somebody's garden. The house is about thirty yards away and you can see a woman in the kitchen. She has not seen you. On the other side of the fence you can see masses of your favourite fruit – strawberries? If you squat down, you can reach through the fence to the fruit and be out of sight of the woman in the house. However, you'll have to dump some of the fruit you've already scrumped. Do you now scrump some fruit from the woman's garden?

You stroll on your way. A little further on you come to an orchard with trees bearing your favourite fruit. Again the fence is low and easily climbable. Do you now scrump some of your favourite fruit?

NO | YES   *Question ends* |

You take a few steps and stop again. You notice that there are many windfalls lying on the gound. This orchard seems to be very unkempt and overgrown. The trees seem to be straggly and long unpruned. The fence here is mostly missing; what there is of it is rusty, dilapidated and long past repair. Do you now scrump some of your favourite fruit?

QUESTION 209

You are walking down the street one bright day. Suddenly you hear a woman shout from down a side-street. You hear running footsteps. Rounding a corner in front of you sprints a youth. He is clutching a woman's handbag. Close behind the youth comes a young policeman in full pursuit. The youth is not very big, about twenty years old, white, and looking frightened. However, he is faster than the policeman who is about twenty yards away. The youth is running along the pavement directly towards you. There is nobody else near. Do you try to help the policeman by attempting to stop or slow down the youth?

 YES

 NO

YES column:

The youth crashes into you and you both fall to the pavement. The policeman arrives and grapples with the youth who looks terrified. He seems to give up. You are on your feet as the policeman drags the youth to his feet. Suddenly, the policeman clutches his side. There is blood. The policeman sags to one knee but still clings to the leg of the struggling youth. The youth turns to strike the policeman again. You can see a short knife in his hand. Do you again intervene to try to help the policeman?

YES | NO   Question ends |

Back to the original incident when the youth first comes sprinting around the corner. This time, there is no policeman in pursuit. There is nobody but you and the youth clutching the handbag. There has been no incident with any knife. Do you still try to stop the youth?

NO column:

The youth is getting very near. The policeman shouts to you to stop him, saying that he has just hit an elderly lady and possibly caused her serious injury. Do you now try to help the policeman by attempting to stop or slow down the youth?

 NO | **YES   Question ends** |

As the youth passes you, he laughs, spits in your face, and calls you chicken. Do you now attempt to stop or slow him down before he makes good his escape?

QUESTION 210

Your firm is holding a fancy dress party. All staff are expected to attend and the staff notice gives details of a fancy dress hire shop. However, you are short of cash and decide to make your own costume. Just before the event, you receive further instructions from your employer: the party is being thrown in honour of a Polish group with whom your company has important business and you are instructed to be available to mix with some of the group and look after them. Do you hire a costume after all?

YES

NO

It is the day before the party and since this is the only such place in town, there are few costumes left. The only one that fits you is a Russian army uniform. All the other remaining outfits are far too small. Do you hire the uniform rather than revert to your plan to make your own?

YES | **NO** *Question ends* |

The same situation, except that the only uniform available is that of a Nazi SS officer. Do you hire this costume?

Your boss is in your office discussing some work and, in passing, asks what you will be wearing to the party. When he hears that you are making your own costume, he seems a little dubious, stresses the importance of the Polish business and suggests that you hire something. Do you follow his suggestion and hire a costume?

NO | **YES** *Question ends* |

You discover that everyone else in the office has hired rather elaborate costumes. You are the only one making their own. Do you now hire a costume?

QUESTION 211 (non-vegetarian)

You are travelling abroad in distant countries. You meet a local family who are very friendly and take you under their wing. They help you in countless ways and, one evening, you are invited to their home for a special meal in your honour. The first dish is announced as a local delicacy. It is cooked rat. To refuse to eat it would be viewed as a slight on your hosts' hospitality. Do you eat the rat?

 YES
 NO

In this instance, the local delicacy presented to you looks suspiciously like, and in fact turns out to be, sheep's eyeballs. Do you eat these?

—Another time, another place. The local delicacy offered for your delectation is snake. Cooked, of course. Do you eat this?

YES | NO *Question ends*

NO | YES *Question ends*

Another place, another time. The delicacy presented to you is raw monkey's brain. Would you eat this?

In this instance, the local delicacy presented in your honour is octopus braised in its own ink. Would you eat this?

QUESTION 212

You are in the greengrocer's doing a spot of shopping, just a pound of potatoes, in fact. You are not in any particular hurry. There are other people in the shop. The assistant asks you what you want. However, there is a middle-aged man there who was actually in the shop before you. He is perfectly ordinary and is unaware of the situation. Do you point out to the assistant that he was next in the queue?

YES

NO

The same situation, except that service has been very slow. You have already had to wait. You are not in a hurry but have grown impatient. Do you still tell the assistant that the man is next?

A little later you are in another shop which is also quite crowded. A woman in front of you is asked by the assistant what she wants. She, however, says that she thinks you were next. You know that the woman was in front of you in the queue. Do you say so?

YES | **NO**   *Question ends* |

You are in the bank when the same thing happens. You just want to cash a cheque. However, you can see that the man who should be next has a whole wad of cheques and a paying-in book. He looks as though he will keep the teller occupied for quite some time. Do you still point out that he is next?

NO | **YES**   *Question ends* |

On another occasion, you are at the bar in a pub waiting to be served. Next to you is someone of the opposite sex whom you like the look of. They have been waiting much longer than you. Amid the confusion, the bartender asks you what you want. Do you point out that this person next to you, who seems to have phlegmatically accepted the situation, is next?

QUESTION 213

Your work takes you abroad for a short spell during which you must live in another country. One of your colleagues there breaks the local laws. You do not know this person very well and neither like nor dislike them. They are of your nationality. The authorities come to ask you some questions. You know that this person is guilty of the crime. If you tell the authorities what you know, your colleague will be convicted. If, on the other hand, you plead ignorance, they cannot even be arrested. There is no possible come-back on you either way. You have taken no part in the crime nor have you benefited from it in any way. The person has killed someone in a brawl. The punishment is life imprisonment – and does mean life – in one of the rather unsavoury local prisons. When the local authorities ask you what you know, do you tell them?

 YES   **NO**

In this instance, their crime is the same but the punishment in this country is execution by beheading. Do you now tell the local authorities what you know?

 YES | NO   *Question ends* |

In this instance, their crime is still the same but the punishment is a nasty form of execution meant to act as a deterrent. The prisoner is tied to a stake in front of a firing squad. The first salvo is aimed at their ankles. The next, at their knees, and so on up their body. Do you now tell the authorities what you know?

The person, in this instance, has not committed murder. Instead, they have been dealing in black-market food and medical supplies intended for a famine-stricken area. The supplies never reached there because of this person. This is viewed locally as theft. The punishment is to chop off the right hand of the prisoner. Do you now tell the authorities what you know?

 NO | YES   *Question ends* |

In this instance, their crime is still that they waylaid food and medical supplies, but the punishment would be three to five years in a local prison. Do you now tell the authorities what you know?

QUESTION 214

Some friends of yours are going on holiday for a month and are looking for someone to house-sit for them. They have a smartish home in an attractive area. They ask you if you know of anyone who could move in for the month. You cannot do it yourself. You only know of one person, another friend of yours, who would be able to house-sit. However, this friend, although extremely honest, is also dirty and not exactly reliable. You are not entirely confident of their suitability to house-sit for your other friends. Do you tell the friends about to go on holiday that you know of somebody?

YES

They ask you what this person is like: whether they are trustworthy, responsible, etc. Do you tell them the plain truth about your friend, rather than glossing over or omitting their defects?

 YES

 | NO   *Question ends* |

After listening to what you have to say, they later meet your friend and agree to leave them in charge of the house. When they return, they find it in chaos. The place is filthy, there are piles of unwashed dishes, cigarette ash everywhere and the house-sitter had obviously held open house for many of his friends. They telephone you, absolutely outraged, and suggest that you should pay for the place to be put to rights. Do you, politely or not, point out that you were perfectly honest with them, that they made the decision themselves and that you refuse to accept any responsibility?

NO

As their holiday nears, your friends become desperate to find anyone who will stay in their house while they are away. Do you now admit knowing of somebody, no matter how unsuitable you think they might be?

NO | YES   *Question ends* |

Your unreliable friend happens to contact you. He has been evicted from where he was living and is homeless. Do you now tell your friends looking for a house-sitter that you know of somebody?

QUESTION 215

Your eight-year-old child has taken up a sport. They need the appropriate clothes and happen to want the colours of their favourite team or individual. You stroll off to the shops to buy the gear. When you get there, you find that the outfits match the originals to the last detail, including the sponsor's name. The one your child wants has the name of a Japanese electronics company plastered right across the front as well as the clothes manufacturer's name. You also find some plain clothes that are the right colour and style but which differ in small details from the 'official' colours your child wants. They also carry no advertising. Both sets of clothes are the same price and quality. Do you buy the one with the advertising?

YES

NO

In this instance, the sponsor is not a Japanese electronics company. Plastered across the front of the sports gear is the name and logo of a company that has had a bad press recently because of its links with South Africa. However, this is the one your child insists on having. Do you still buy the one with the advertising on?

YES | NO   *Question ends* |

As you are about to purchase it, the assistant informs you that in fact the goods are mispriced. The plain ones are actually £2 cheaper. Do you still buy the ones with the advertising on them?

As you are about to make your purchase, the assistant points out that some of the goods are mispriced. The clothes with the sponsor's name on them are £2 cheaper than marked. Do you now buy the ones with the advertising on?

NO | YES   *Question ends* |

Your child is not impressed by your ethics. They don't like the clothes you have bought because they are not the real thing and don't have 'all the proper writing on'. They may wear them under duress but complain that all their friends have the 'right gear'. Do you relent and go back to change the gear?

QUESTION 216

You and a friend are baby-sitting for some close friends. You decide to have a game of Scrabble. Your friends have a fifteen-year-old son who is away at the moment. While rummaging in his room for the Scrabble set you find some soft-core pornographic magazines of the *Penthouse* variety hidden away. Do you inform his parents?

YES

The same situation, except that the magazines you find are extremely left-wing communist ones. You know the parents are Conservatives. Do you tell the parents about their son's magazines?

YES

The same situation, except that the magazines you find are highly racist, Fascist ones. You know the parents are Socialists. Do you tell them about their son's magazines?

NO

The same situation, except that the magazines you find are extremely right-wing Fascist publications. You know the parents are Socialists. Do you tell the parents about their son's magazines?

| NO | *Question ends* |

NO

The same situation, except that the magazines you find are extremely left-wing communist ones. You know the parents are Conservatives. Do you tell them about their son's magazines?

| YES | *Question ends* |

QUESTION 217

You are travelling on the London Tube when it stops at a station. Just as the doors are about to close, you see someone running down the steps on to the platform. They are obviously hoping to catch the train. You are standing right by the nearest doors to them. By simply sticking your foot out you can stop the doors from closing to allow the person to get on the train. The person is perfectly ordinary, in their mid-thirties, wearing smart but casual clothes and of the same sex and colour as you. Do you stop the doors from closing?

YES

In this instance, the person is still the same sex as you but they are about twenty years old. They are dressed in black, have brightly coloured hair and are carrying a Walkman. They do not look aggressive in any way. Do you still hold the doors open?

YES | NO   Question ends |

In this instance, the person is male and a teenager. He is wearing old jeans, a ripped T-shirt and sports a football scarf tied around his waist. He is carrying a can of beer in one hand, but does not seem drunk or aggressive. (If you happen to be a football supporter, he is not sporting your team's colours!) Do you still hold the doors open?

NO

In this instance, the person is still the same sex as you. However, it is a smartly dressed Japanese tourist clutching a guide to London. They call something to you in Japanese as they hurry towards the train. Do you now hold the doors open?

NO | YES   Question ends |

In this instance, the latecomer is a respectably dressed lady in her early sixties. She is carrying a small suitcase and is hurrying as best she can. Do you now hold the door open?

QUESTION 218

It is a cold, miserable, winter's morning. There is an icy sleet falling. You awake with a hangover from a party the night before. There is nothing at work that requires your immediate attention. You are not entitled to any more holiday. Would you phone in to say that you were ill, or make some other excuse, rather than go in?

 YES

 NO

The same situation, except that there is something that requires your immediate attention at work. It should really be done today or else it will be too late. Will you phone in to say that you are ill, or make some other excuse, rather than go in?

The same situation, except that it is a beautiful summer's morning, the best of the year so far. Would you phone in to say you were ill, or make some other excuse, rather than go in?

 NO | **YES** *Question ends* |

 YES | **NO** *Question ends* |

You are paid by the hour. If you don't go in, you don't get paid for that time. The job just brings in enough to get by. Would you phone in to say you were ill, or make some other excuse, rather than go in?

While you are getting ready to go to work, your lover phones and, because it's such a beautiful day, suggests that you both take the day off and go for a picnic in the country. Would you now phone work to say that you were ill, or make some other excuse rather than go in?

QUESTION 219

You have recently moved into a new flat. You have an elderly neighbour who is confined to a wheelchair. Since you have moved in, he has shouted for your assistance on quite a few occasions. When you have gone to help, he has been grumpy and has shown little gratitude. Sometimes he has called you for the most trivial reasons.

It is early one Sunday morning and you are enjoying a well-earned lie-in. You hear your neighbour shouting your name. Do you get up and go and see what he wants?

 YES   **NO**

You throw some clothes on and start off. As you reach your front door, he stops calling. Do you still go to see if you can be of any assistance?

Although he doesn't sound desperate, he continues to shout. You leave it for a few minutes but he continues. Do you now go to see what he wants?

YES | NO   *Question ends* | **NO** | YES   *Question ends* |

When you get down there, you discover that he only wanted the top taken off his ketchup bottle but had managed to do it himself in the end which is why he stopped calling. You return to bed. He begins shouting for you again later that morning. Do you again get up to go and see what is wrong?

You smell burning. It could be his toast as it was on a previous similar occasion. He has gone silent. Do you now go and see if you can be of any assistance?

QUESTION 220

You are playing in a mid-season league squash match for your club. It is the last point of the game, which you win with a stretching shot. However, you know that it was an illegal shot and that the ball was 'not up'. The referee awards you the match. Your opponent is only one point in arrears. Do you decline the point, admitting that the ball was 'not up'?

YES

NO

As you turn to tell the referee, you realize that quite a crowd had in fact gathered to watch as the match was so close and exciting. The club captain and supporters are all now cheering wildly and shouting congratulations from the balcony. Do you still admit that the last 'match-winning' shot was 'not up'?

Your opponent is very upset and contests the decision with the referee. He is adamant that the ball was 'not up' and that it is daylight robbery. Your opponent asks you directly in front of the referee whether you thought the ball was up or not. Do you admit that it wasn't?

YES | **NO**   *Question ends* |

NO | **YES**   *Question ends* |

In this instance, the match is not a mid-season but a vital end-of-season one. During the course of the game, your opponent was given two dubious lets, which you felt were unsporting but you accepted the referee's decision. The crowd on the balcony is cheering wildly as your victory has given your club the championship for the first time in its history. Do you decline the point, admitting that the shot was 'not up'?

The referee awards you the match. You are in the bar having a quiet drink afterwards when the referee comes in. He joins you. There is nobody else around. Over a drink, he confesses that he had been unsighted, and smilingly asks, since it now makes no difference, if the ball was up or not. Do you now admit that the ball was 'not up'?

QUESTION 221

You are rummaging through your bags one day when you come across a piece of paper. Written on it, in your writing, is a telephone number. It looks quite recent but there is no name or anything else to identify it. You cannot recall to whom the number might belong. Do you phone it to find out?

 YES　　　　　　　　　　 **NO**

It turns out to be somebody's home. You speak to the person. You do not know them, nor do they know you. Neither of you can think of any reason why you have their number. The person is the opposite sex to you and seems very amicable. In fact, since it turns out that they do not live too far away, they suggest that the two of you meet up for a drink and a chat to see if you can discover the reason for your having their phone number. Would you agree to meet them?

In this instance, there is a name by the phone number. The name means nothing to you. It is the name of somebody of the same sex as you. Would you now phone the number to find out why you have noted it down?

 NO　　　　| **YES**　*Question ends* |

This time, the name is of someone of the opposite sex to you. Would you now phone it?

 YES　　　　| **NO**　*Question ends* |

In this instance, you find the number on a piece of paper folded inside a notebook that you have not used for about six months. Do you still phone the number?

QUESTION 222

You are on a first date with someone you find very attractive. You are in a fairly smart restaurant where neither of you has been before, although you have heard good reports. The meal will cost about £18 to £20. The starters are fine but when you get your main course, it is tough and somewhat stringy. The restaurant is fairly busy. Do you complain to your waiter?

 YES

 NO

In this instance, the restaurant specializes in a foreign cuisine that neither of you has tried before. It could be that the main course is meant to be as it is. Do you still complain to your waiter?

There is nobody else in the restaurant. The waiter passes by your table and stops to enquire whether everything is satisfactory. Do you now complain to your waiter?

 YES | **NO** *Question ends* |

 NO | **YES** *Question ends* |

You are trying to attract the waiter's attention. He is very self-confident and is laughing and joking with other customers. He is clearly very popular with the regular clients and it will obviously be some time before he is free. Do you still complain?

You mention the fact that your main course is tough and stringy to your partner. Your partner remarks, 'So that's what they were talking about!' Your partner than explains that, when they went to the toilet earlier, they passed the kitchen. The door was slightly open and they heard someone say something like, 'Oh, don't worry. That will do for them.' Do you now complain to your waiter?

QUESTION 223 (female)

You are on a London Tube in the rush-hour. The compartment is crowded with travellers and you have to stand. After a while, you begin to suspect that you are not simply being brushed against by other passengers; someone behind you seems to be deliberately but gently fondling your posterior – though you can't be certain it's intentional. The crush is so great that it is virtually impossible for you to turn and identify the culprit. The next stop is the point at which you will be leaving the train. Do you say anything?

YES

NO

Just then, the crowd eases a fraction enabling you to turn quickly to face your suspected assailant. You come face to face with a pair of youngish men who grin at you knowingly. One of them makes a comment to the other in what sounds like Italian. They both laugh. They then smile at you warmly. Do you now voice any complaint?

YES

| NO   Question ends |

If this had all happened on a crowded bus in the centre of Rome, would you still voice your complaint?

The movements become more deliberate. You are no longer in any doubt that your rear is being covertly fondled. It is not far to the next stop where you will be leaving the train. Do you voice any complaint?

NO

| YES   Question ends |

The same situation, except that you have another twenty minutes' ride on the train before your destination. Do you now voice any complaint?

QUESTION 224

It is a bright, pleasant, sunny day. You are on your way to work a little early and in no great hurry. Ahead of you, you can see some flag-sellers obviously raising money for some cause. One approaches you. You can see the stickers and their money tin. They are raising money for a charity concerned with helping homeless immigrants to this country. You have never heard of the organization before. You have plenty of change in your pocket. Do you put some money in the tin?

 YES   **NO**

| The same situation, except that the collectors are trying to raise money for an organization raising money to help publicize the plight of political dissidents in Russia. Do you put any money in the tin? | The same situation, except that this time the collectors are raising money for an organization involved in raising money to help the most desperate of the unemployed in this country. Do you put any money in this tin? |

 YES | NO *Question ends* | **NO** | YES *Question ends* |

The same situation, except that the collectors belong to some religious cult of which you have never heard. They are raising money for their own organization. Do you put any money in this tin?

The same situation, except that the collectors are raising money for a national charity, of which you have heard, which provides help for the elderly and infirm. Do you put any money in this tin?

QUESTION 225

You are at work with a large company which has always treated you and the rest of the staff with great fairness. You have never had any cause for complaint. You are planning a party and wish to make some fancy invitations. In the office stationery cupboard are some items of graphic equipment which you would need to do this. These are quite expensive and would cost you about £10 if you were to buy them in the shops. Do you pilfer them from the office?

 YES   **NO**

There are many other items around the office which you could happily use at home, such as staplers, box files, calculators, etc. Would you pilfer such items from your office if you needed them?

 YES | NO   *Question ends* |

There are several larger items around the office such as portable typewriters, and other items of that size and value. Would you be prepared to pilfer any of these that you needed at home?

The office supplies some felt-tipped pens and transparent tape. Would you pilfer small items like these for use at home?

 NO | **YES**   *Question ends* |

The office has a franking machine and a book of stamps for sending out office correspondence. Would you use any of these facilities to send out your personal mail?

QUESTION 226

You are at a private showing in a small art gallery. You have gone along with some friends for an evening out and the free drink. You've wandered around and looked at the various paintings. You don't know the artist, nor do your friends. Also, you don't like the paintings in the least. You happen to be standing in front of one that you think is particularly bad, when someone you don't know comes up beside you, nods at the painting and asks you what you think of it. You haven't the faintest idea who this person is. You do know that the artist and many of the artist's friends are present as is the gallery owner and potential purchasers of the paintings. The person is the same sex as you, and judging from the artist's name, the same sex as the artist. There is nobody else in earshot. Do you, tactfully or otherwise, give your true opinion?

 YES

 NO

Just then, somebody calls to this person by name. It is the artist whose works are on the walls. They have a quick word with the person who called them and then turn to you again. Do you still express your true opinion?

 YES   **NO** *Question ends*

There is another interruption. The artist is collared by the gallery owner to talk to a potential purchaser. Someone else comes up to you and introduces themselves. They are the artist's partner. In chatting to them, you learn that this is the artist's first showing, how hard they have worked and how worried they are as to how well the work will go down. After a bit, they wander off again. The artist rejoins you and asks you what you think. Do you still express your true opinion?

Before you can actually say anything, somebody hails this person and has a quick word with them. It transpires that they are an art lecturer at the college where the artist studied. The brief conversation finishes and the interloper goes off. The lecturer apologizes for the interruption and asks you to continue with what you were about to say. Do you now express your true opinion?

 NO   **YES** *Question ends*

A little later, you are talking to the artist. They have just asked what you think of their work when somebody comes over and congratulates them saying that they think the work is marvellous. As they leave, the artist looks to the ceiling and says, 'God! I hate these dos. Everyone's so damned patronizing.' Do you now express your true opinion?

QUESTION 227

If you had slept with anyone in this room *before* you met your current partner, would you have admitted it to your current partner if they had asked you?

 YES   **NO**

If you had slept with anyone in this room *since* you met your current partner, would you have admitted it to your current partner if they had asked you?

 YES | **NO**   *Question ends* |

Would you have told them about either instance if they had not asked you and would otherwise never have known?

The person whom you have slept with is asked if they have slept with anyone in this room and they have answered yes. Your partner knows you were once very friendly with this person before you got together with your current partner. Your partner later accuses you directly in private, stating in positive terms that you have and they always suspected it. Do you now admit it?

 NO | **YES**   *Question ends* |

Your partner is upset for a long time and still refuses to believe you. Your relationship is deteriorating and you realize that the only way to save the situation is to tell the truth or you will lose your partner, whom you love very much. Do you now tell the truth when they ask you for the very last time?

QUESTION 228

It is 7.30 on a Saturday evening. You have been doing a spot of decoration and the place is in a bit of a mess. You are very tired after a hard day and are relaxing in a good hot bath.

You've just got out of the bath and slipped on some clothes when the doorbell rings. You answer it to find four close friends armed with some bottles of wine. You are very tired and do not feel like any company. Do you tell them that you are tired and to go away?

 YES

 NO

As you start to tell them, they apologize and say that they hope that they are not too early for dinner. It suddenly dawns on you that you had invited them round and completely forgotten about it. Do you still tell them the truth and ask them to go?

 YES | NO *Question ends* |

You're back to just getting out of the bath when the doorbell rings. However, this time it is some acquaintances from some distance away whom you had met during a weekend in the country. You had told them to pop round when they were down your way. It would seem that now is the hour. Do you ask them to leave?

In this instance, when you answer the door it is not a group of close friends but one very close friend. They have just broken up with their partner and have been depressed. However, you have seen a bit too much of them lately and have become tired of the current bouts of soul-searching, regrets, etc., etc. Although you are very fond of them, you are not in the mood for another session tonight. Do you ask them to go away?

NO | YES *Question ends* |

In this instance, when you answer the door it is not a close friend but a neighbour, who is very zealous in community action. Although you are not particularly friendly, your neighbour often pops round to discuss local action on the state of the pavements, overhanging trees, the neighbourhood watch scheme, and so on. He tells you that he would like to ask your opinion on something, and could he come in to discuss it. Do you tell him to go away?

QUESTION 229

You are walking along the street when you notice a bracelet lying in the gutter. It looks quite expensive and you estimate that you could get about £50 for it. You are not hard up, but neither are you rolling in money. The nearest police station is about half a mile away. Do you hand the bracelet in to the police?

 YES

 NO

On the way to the police station, you inspect the bracelet more closely. You see some old-looking hallmarks. You realize that the bracelet is more valuable than you had thought. You could probably get about £300 for it. Do you still hand it in to the police?

On closer inspection, you can see that it is vastly more valuable than you had thought. It has some old-looking hallmarks and the many tiny jewels look real. It could well be worth thousands. Do you now hand it in to the police?

 YES    | NO   *Question ends* |

 NO | YES   *Question ends* |

The same situation, except that on close inspection you can see that the bracelet is in fact rather cheap and shoddy. It is probably only worth a few pounds at the very most. Do you now hand it in to the police?

In this instance, the bracelet is not worth thousands, it is the £50 variety again. However, when you pick it up, you can see that it is very small. When you compare it to your wrist, it is evident that the bracelet is a child's. Do you now hand it in to the police?

QUESTION 230

You have decided to sell your car. You place an advertisement in the local paper. From the responses, you agree a price with one of the people and promise them that the car is theirs. No money has yet changed hands. A little later a friend comes round and says that they saw your advertisement but have been unable to get in touch with you. They would very much have liked to buy your car but can offer no more than the price you have already agreed with the stranger. Do you break your promise to the stranger and, instead, promise to sell the car to your friend?

 YES

 NO

At this point, the telephone rings. It is the person to whom you had promised the car. When you tell them that you will not be selling them the car, they increase their offer by £200. Your friend, who is still there, indicates that he cannot match this offer. Do you now break your promise to your friend and agree to sell it to the stranger?

The situation is the same, except that the friend is someone who once did you a great favour that you have never had the opportunity to repay. Would you now break your promise to the stranger and, instead, promise the car to your friend?

 YES

 NO | **YES**   *Question ends* |

Before you complete the deal with the stranger, your friend returns and says that he can increase his offer by £150 – £50 short of the stranger's offer. Do you now go back on your agreement with the stranger and sell the car to your friend?

Your friend goes away but returns shortly. He says that he has managed to raise some money and can now increase the offer by £200. Do you now break your promise to the stranger and sell the car to your friend?

| **NO**   *Question ends* |

258

QUESTION 231

You are single. You have had one night of passion at a party which you hope might develop into a more lasting relationship. Just before the party you had noticed some rather ominous symptoms but had shrugged them off as just another minor irritation. However, they don't go away and get worse. When you go to the doctor he diagnoses a mild, but virulent, strain of VD. He prescribes treatment and tells you that it is very important that you inform anyone you have slept with over the past six months that they may have this infection. Do you contact the person you met at the party and tell them to go for a check-up?

 YES **NO**

When you phone, and before you have had time to say anything, they say that they have been trying to contact you to invite you out for a meal. You accept and have a wonderful evening. Do you tell them about the doctor's diagnosis now?

 YES | NO *Question ends*

You have led quite a promiscuous life over the past year in your search for that elusive steady relationship. Your embarrassing news is accepted with good grace but when you are asked whether you have slept with others before, do you tell the truth?

The person you met at the party invites you out for a meal and later takes you back to their place for a drink. They tell you that they would love you to stay but have been suffering from some rather strange and embarrassing symptoms lately and that it wouldn't be wise. Do you say that you have had a mild form of VD diagnosed and may have passed it on when you could let them go on thinking that they may have passed it on to you?

 NO | YES *Question ends*

You grow even more attracted to your new partner. However they are clearly terribly embarrassed about this complaint and keep insisting that they aren't good enough for you. A few weeks later, they tell you that they can't go on seeing you and that they couldn't be happy in such an unequal relationship. Do you now say that, in fact, you passed it on to them?

QUESTION 232

Your partner has just prepared a sumptuous three-course meal which you are both about to sit down and enjoy. The telephone rings. Your partner is busy placing the meal on the table. You have no telephone answering machine and the phone continues to ring. You go to answer it. The meal is spoiling by the second. It is a close friend whom you haven't seen for ages phoning for a chat. Do you make excuses quickly and arrange to call back rather than talking now?

 YES

 NO

In this instance, the phone call turns out to be from your boss who has phoned to sound you out on a possible promotion that will involve more interesting work and better money. Do you still make your excuses rather than talking now?

In this instance, your partner has just cooked your favourite soufflé. It will be as flat as a pancake in seconds. Do you now make your excuses?

 YES

| NO · Question ends |

 NO

| YES   *Question ends* |

In this instance, the call is from one of your parents to tell you that a relative has been taken into hospital. It is not a particularly close relative, nor one that you see often or like much. Do you still, however tactfully, make your excuses rather than talking now?

In this instance, you are the cook. You have timed everything to perfection. If you stop to talk on the phone, the fruit of your labours will all be overdone and spoilt. Would you now make your excuses?

QUESTION 233

You receive a letter from a friend who explains that they have used your name as a referee for a job that thay have applied for. They explain that they tried to contact you beforehand but were unable to get in touch with you. They apologize and hope you won't mind. Before you can speak to them, you receive a letter from the company to which your friend has applied. Much as you like your friend, you do not have a very high opinion of their professional competence. The company that they have applied to is a large multinational conglomerate. You actually feel that your friend is not up to the job. Do you, in so many words, say so in your reference?

YES

NO

Before you can actually write the reference, your friend manages to get in touch with you. They are very depressed and reveal that they were dismissed from their previous job and are now relying on this new one to keep up their mortgage repayments, etc. Regardless of anything you say, your friend is adamant that they want you to write the reference as there is nobody else. When you write it, do you still say, in so many words, that you do not think that your friend is up to the job?

YES | NO   *Question ends* |

The situation differs in that you run your own small company. It turns out that your friend has applied for a job with your only competitor, who has in the past used some cut-throat methods against you. If your friend gets the job, they would be running the department that is actually in the most direct conflict with you. For one reason or another, the company seeking the reference does not know that you, the referee, are their competitor, nor will they be any the wiser when you send the reference. Do you still say, in so many words, that your friend is not suitable for the job?

Despite your efforts, your friend does not get the job. Some days later, you are at work when the personnel manager calls you. Your friend has applied for a job with your company and again quoted you as a referee. Your personnel manager asks you how suitable for the job you think your friend is. Again, you do not think that they are up to it. Do you, in so many words, say so to your personnel manager?

NO | YES   *Question ends* |

Your friend gets the job but a few months later it has become clear to all concerned that they are hopelessly incompetent. Your boss is rather angry that you should have endorsed them. Rather than brazen it out by saying that you believed that they would be suitable, do you admit that you genuinely doubted their suitability all along?

QUESTION 234

You are walking home along the riverside. As you pass a weir, you can see a bedraggled cat lying half in the water and half on the river-bank. It is miaowing plaintively and is obviously exhausted and in imminent danger of being swept off towards the weir. The river-bank is steep, muddy and slippery. You are wearing some old casual clothes. There is no one else around as far as you can see. Do you go down the river-bank to try and save the cat?

 YES

 NO

As you slither down the bank, the cat is swept away into deep water and towards the weir. The only way to save it now would be to dive into the river and swim. However, the current is fairly strong and there are danger signs warning against swimming in this stretch of the river. Do you still attempt to save the cat?

A woman suddenly rushes out of a side-street. She is in a near panic as she explains that she's been trying to find someone to save her prize Persian which has fallen into the river. She is obviously well off. Do you now go down the river-bank to try to save the cat?

 YES | NO   *Question ends* |

 NO | YES   *Question ends* |

You reach the cat but the current is stronger than you thought. You cannot swim against it *and* hold the cat. If you do not release it, you will be swept to the weir. The weir is quite high and there is an obvious risk of injury if you were to go over. However, the only way to save the cat would be to chance going over the weir while holding it. Do you still try to save the cat?

The woman adds that she will gladly reward you with an all expenses paid, two-month holiday in her villa in the South of France. Do you now attempt to save the cat?

QUESTION 235

It is approaching Christmas. You get a Christmas card from some old friends whom you have not seen for many years as they have moved abroad. They were not close friends, merely acquaintances, and your only communication has been the exchange of Christmas cards. You have already sent all your cards and you had chosen, for reasons of your own, to omit these people this year. You have some spare cards left. Do you send them a card?

YES

NO

The same situation, except that you have no spare cards handy, also you have lost their address. You know some other friends whom you could phone to find out the address. Do you take the trouble to get the address, buy a card and send it to them?

The situation is the same, except that you had not deliberately chosen to omit these people. You had simply forgotten that they even existed. Do you send them a card on receiving theirs?

NO

YES | Question ends |

YES

| NO   *Question ends* |

The same situation, except that the card you receive is from someone you only met recently. You did not particularly like them, although you exchanged addresses. You had not even thought of sending them a card when you sent yours. Do you now go and buy a card to send to them in return?

The situation is the same, except that the unexpected card is from someone that you only recently met. You did not particularly like them and have not sent them a card. However, they do have a large house with a swimming pool and their card bears a message saying that they would be delighted to see you some time. Do you send them a card now?

QUESTION 236

You live near a college. You have a spare room and you are so short of cash that you must take in a summer student for six weeks to make ends meet. You have no alternative. You contact the college and find that there are only two students still without summer accommodation. You meet them both. They are of the same foreign nationality, the same sex as you, the same colour as you, equally affable, friendly, etc. In essence, they are identical in all respects *except* one is Roman Catholic and the other is Jewish. Do you toss a coin or use some other random method to decide who is to rent the room rather than choosing yourself?

YES

NO

In this instance, one is a Mormon and the other is a Jehovah's Witness. Do you still toss the coin?

In this instance, one is Muslim and the other is Jewish. Would you now toss a coin?

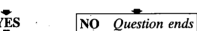

YES | NO   *Question ends* | **NO** | YES   *Question ends* |

In this instance, one is Roman Catholic and the other is Protestant. However, both are from Northern Ireland. Do you still toss the coin?

In this instance, one is Roman Catholic and the other is Protestant. Would you now toss a coin?

QUESTION 237

Your work takes you abroad for a short spell during which you must live in another country. The authorities approach you to ask questions about someone you happen to know. This person is a native of the country in which you are working. You do not know them particularly well and you neither like nor dislike them. You know the person is guilty of the crime. If you tell the authorities what you know, the person will be convicted. If, on the other hand, you plead ignorance, they cannot even be arrested. There is no possible come-back on you either way. You have taken no part in the crime nor have you benefited from it in any way. The person is a local man who has committed a particularly nasty and preplanned murder of a rival trader. However, the punishment in this country is death by beheading. When the local authorities come to ask you what you know, do you tell them?

 YES   **NO**

In this instance, the crime is the same but the punishment is a nasty form of execution designed to act as a deterrent. The prisoner is tied to a stake in front of a firing squad. The first salvo is aimed at their ankles. The next, at their knees, and so on up their body in stages. Do you still tell the local authorities what you know when they ask?

The crime is the same but the punishment is death by hanging. Do you now tell the local authorities what you know when they ask?

 NO | **YES** *Question ends* |

NO | **YES** *Question ends* |

The crime is still the same but the punishment is life imprisonment. Do you now tell the local authorities what you know when they ask?

In this instance, the person is a woman. Her crime is adultery and the punishment is to be stoned to death. Do you still tell the authorities what you know when they ask?

END NOTE

Many of the dilemmas in this book are based on true stories. Even some of the more outlandish ones. If you know of any true dilemmas that you think would be interesting, please formulate them into the style of the questions in this book and send them to the author, care of Penguin Books. If there is sufficient response, you may find your contribution published in a second volume of *On the Spot*. All such contributions would, of course, be acknowledged and receive payment if published.

MORE ABOUT PENGUINS, PELICANS, PEREGRINES AND PUFFINS

For further information about books available from Penguins please write to Dept EP, Penguin Books Ltd, Harmondsworth, Middlesex UB7 0DA.

In the U.S.A.: For a complete list of books available from Penguins in the United States write to Dept DG, Penguin Books, 299 Murray Hill Parkway, East Rutherford, New Jersey 07073.

In Canada: For a complete list of books available from Penguins in Canada write to Penguin Books Canada Ltd, 2801 John Street, Markham, Ontario L3R 1B4.

In Australia: For a complete list of books available from Penguins in Australia write to the Marketing Department, Penguin Books Australia Ltd, P.O. Box 257, Ringwood, Victoria 3134.

In New Zealand: For a complete list of books available from Penguins in New Zealand write to the Marketing Department, Penguin Books (N.Z.) Ltd, Private Bag, Takapuna, Auckland 9.

In India: For a complete list of books available from Penguins in India write to Penguin Overseas Ltd, 706 Eros Apartments, 56 Nehru Place, New Delhi 110019.

PENGUINS ON HEALTH, SPORT AND KEEPING FIT

☐ **Audrey Eyton's F-Plus**

F-Plan menus for women who lunch at work * snack eaters * keen cooks * freezer-owners * busy dieters using convenience foods * overweight children * drinkers and non-drinkers. 'Your short-cut to the most sensational diet of the century' – *Daily Express*

☐ **The F-Plan Calorie Counter and Fibre Chart Audrey Eyton**

An indispensable companion to the F-Plan diet. High-fibre fresh, canned and packaged foods are listed, there's a separate chart for drinks, *plus* a wonderful selection of effortless F-Plan meals.

☐ **The Parents A–Z Penelope Leach**

From the expert author of *Baby & Child*, this skilled, intelligent and comprehensive guide is by far the best reference book currently available for parents, whether your children are six months, six or sixteen years.

☐ **Woman's Experience of Sex Sheila Kitzinger**

Fully illustrated with photographs and line drawings, this book explores the riches of women's sexuality at every stage of life. 'A book which any mother could confidently pass on to her daughter – and her partner too' – *Sunday Times*

☐ **Alternative Medicine Andrew Stanway**

From Acupuncture and Alexander Technique to Macrobiotics and Yoga, Dr Stanway provides an informed and objective guide to thirty-two therapies in alternative medicine.

☐ **Pregnancy Dr Jonathan Scher and Carol Dix**

Containing the most up-to-date information on pregnancy – the effects of stress, sexual intercourse, drugs, diet, late maternity and genetic disorders – this book is an invaluable and reassuring guide for prospective parents.

PENGUINS ON HEALTH, SPORT AND KEEPING FIT

☐ *Medicines* **Peter Parish**

Fifth Edition. The usages, dosages and adverse effects of all medicines obtainable on prescription or over the counter are covered in this reference guide, designed for the ordinary reader and everyone in health care.

☐ *Baby & Child* **Penelope Leach**

A fully illustrated, expert and comprehensive handbook on the first five years of life. 'It stands head and shoulders above anything else available at the moment' – Mary Kenny in the *Spectator*

☐ *Vogue Natural Health and Beauty*
Bronwen Meredith

Health foods, yoga, spas, recipes, natural remedies and beauty preparations are all included in this superb, fully illustrated guide and companion to the bestselling *Vogue Body and Beauty Book.*

☐ *Pregnancy and Diet* **Rachel Holme**

With suggested foods, a sample diet-plan of menus and advice on nutrition, this guide shows you how to avoid excessive calories but still eat well and healthily during pregnancy.

☐ *The Penguin Bicycle Handbook* **Rob van der Plas**

Choosing a bicycle, maintenance, accessories, basic tools, safety, keeping fit – all these subjects and more are covered in this popular, fully illustrated guide to the total bicycle lifestyle.

☐ *Physical Fitness*

Containing the 5BX 11-minute-a-day plan for men and the XBX 12-minute-a-day plan for women, this book illustrates the famous programmes originally developed by the Royal Canadian Air Force and now used successfully all over the world.

COOKERY AND GARDENING IN PENGUINS

☐ *Italian Food* **Elizabeth David**

'The great book on Italian cooking in English' – Hugh Johnson. 'Certainly the best book we know dealing not only with the food but with the wines of Italy' – *Wine and Food*

☐ *An Invitation to Indian Cooking* **Madhur Jaffrey**

A witty, practical and irresistible handbook on Indian cooking by the presenter of the highly successful BBC television series.

☐ *The Pastry Book* **Rosemary Wadey**

From Beef Wellington to Treacle Tart and Cream-filled Eclairs – here are sweet and savoury recipes for all occasions, plus expert advice that should give you winning results every time.

☐ *The Cottage Garden* **Anne Scott-James**

'Her history is neatly and simply laid out; well-stocked with attractive illustrations' – *The Times.* 'The garden book I have most enjoyed reading in the last few years' – *Observer*

☐ *Chinese Food* **Kenneth Lo**

The popular, step-by-step introduction to the philosophy, practice, menus and delicious recipes of Chinese cooking.

☐ *The Cuisine of the Rose* **Mireille Johnston**

Classic French cooking from Burgundy and Lyonnais, explained with the kind of flair, atmosphere and enthusiasm that only the most exciting cookbooks possess.

COOKERY AND GARDENING
IN PENGUINS

☐ **The Magic Garden** Shirley Conran

The gardening book for the absolute beginner. 'Whether you have a window box, a patio, an acre or a cabbage patch . . . you will enjoy this' – *Daily Express*

☐ **Mediterranean Cookbook** Arabella Boxer

A gastronomic grand tour of the region: 'The best book on Mediterranean cookery I have read since Elizabeth David' – *Sunday Express*

☐ **Favourite Food** Josceline Dimbleby

These superb recipes, all favourites among Josceline Dimbleby's family and friends, make up 'an inspiration to anyone who likes to be really creative in the kitchen' – Delia Smith

☐ **The Chocolate Book** Helge Rubinstein

Part cookery book, part social history, this sumptuous book offers an unbeatable selection of recipes – chocolate cakes, ice-creams, pies, truffles, drinks and savoury dishes galore.

☐ **Good Healthy Food** Gail Duff

Mushrooms in Sherry, Lamb with Lemon and Tarragon, Strawberry and Soured Cream Mousse . . . You'll find that all the dishes here are tempting and delicious to taste, as well as being healthy to eat.

☐ **The Adventurous Gardener** Christopher Lloyd

Prejudiced, delightful and always stimulating, Christopher Lloyd's book is essential reading for everyone who loves gardening. 'Get it and enjoy it' – *Financial Times*

PENGUIN REFERENCE BOOKS

☐ **The Penguin Map of the World**

Clear, colourful, crammed with information and fully up-to-date, this is a useful map to stick on your wall at home, at school or in the office.

☐ **The Penguin Map of Europe**

Covers all land eastwards to the Urals, southwards to North Africa and up to Syria, Iraq and Iran * Scale = 1:5,500,000 * 4-colour artwork * Features main roads, railways, oil and gas pipelines, plus extra information including national flags, currencies and populations.

☐ **The Penguin Map of the British Isles**

Including the Orkneys, the Shetlands, the Channel Islands and much of Normandy, this excellent map is ideal for planning routes and touring holidays, or as a study aid.

☐ **The Penguin Dictionary of Quotations**

A treasure-trove of over 12,000 new gems and old favourites, from Aesop and Matthew Arnold to Xenophon and Zola.

☐ **The Penguin Dictionary of Art and Artists**

Fifth Edition. 'A vast amount of information intelligently presented, carefully detailed, abreast of current thought and scholarship and easy to read' – *The Times Literary Supplement*

☐ **The Penguin Pocket Thesaurus**

A pocket-sized version of Roget's classic, and an essential companion for all commuters, crossword addicts, students, journalists and the stuck-for-words.